Heikki Mikkeli

# An Aristotelian Response to Renaissance Humanism:

Jacopo Zabarella on the Nature
of Arts and Sciences

Societas Historica Finlandiae
Suomen Historiallinen Seura
Finska Historiska Samfundet


Studia Historica 41

Heikki Mikkeli

# An Aristotelian Response to Renaissance Humanism:
## Jacopo Zabarella on the Nature of Arts and Sciences

 SHS/Helsinki/1992

Cover:    Rauno Endén
Painting: Main entrance of the University of Padua (Palazzo del Bò).
          Engraving from the 17th century. Published in "I secoli d'oro
          della Medicina" 1986.

The Finnish Historical Society has published this study with the
permission, granted on 24 March 1992, of Helsinki University, Faculty of
Arts.

Keywords:  History of Science – Renaissance Aristotelianism – Jacopo
           Zabarella

ISSN 0081-6493
ISBN 951-8915-58-X

Gummerus Kirjapaino Oy
Jyväskylä 1992

# Contents

# Acknowledgments

Many individuals and several institutions have helped me on my way. First of all, I would like to thank Professor Simo Knuuttila who encouraged me to study Renaissance Aristotelianism. Without his generosity in sharing his learning I would not have been able to accomplish my task. I am also grateful for his comments on a manuscript of this book.

I would also like to thank all those at the History Department of the University of Helsinki who provided me with assistance and advice, especially Professors Anto Leikola, Päivi Setälä and Pekka Suvanto. During the years 1986-1987 I worked for a project lead by Associate Professor Matti Viikari, who as my adviser has constantly given me valuable criticism.

In 1988–1990 I had the priviledge to hold the post of research associate of the Academy of Finland and I am grateful to the Research Council for the Humanities for their confidence. During the last five years the Renvall Institute of Historical Research has kindly provided me with working facilities. I would also like to thank Jenny and Antti Wihuri Foundation, Väinö Tanner Foundation and Finnish Cultural Fund (Päivi Priha Foundation) for their financial support.

The staffs of various institutes and libraries in Italy and elsewhere have promptly helped me in my studies. In particular I wish to thank the staff of Villa Lante, the Finnish Institute in Rome, and the staff of the Helsinki University Library whose kind attitude made it a memorable pleasure to deal with them. I would also like to express my gratitude to the Finnish Historical Society for giving the permission to print this study in their series, and especially to Rauno Endén, for bringing it into its final published form.

The English language of this thesis was painstakingly corrected by Gillian Day, MA. Due to later additions and changes, I can claim sole responsibility for those weaknesses and errors which remain. It is impossible to name all friends who have helped me in the long process of making this study. However, during the last few years the help of Markku Peltonen, Kari Saastamoinen and Ilkka Turunen has been particularly valuable.

Finally, I would like to mention those nearest to me. My mother Anna-Liisa and my late father Mikko taught me to love learning and I am grateful for their encouragement and generosity. However, my greatest debt is to my family. My wife Jaana Iso-Markku and our children, Antti and Outi, provided companionship I needed to see me through a project that at times seemed boundless.

Helsinki, on Easter Monday 1992

# 1. Introduction

## 1.1. Humanism and science

Peter Burke has distinguished two principal uses of the word humanism; one precise and narrow, and the other rather wide and vague. According to him, humanism in the wider sense is associated with belief in the dignity of man and, more generally, with human and secular values. These became the subject of several treatises in the Italian Renaissance. On the other hand, historians tend nowadays to restrict the term humanism to refer to the men known in *Quattrocento* Italy as *humanistae*, in other words the teachers of the *studia humanitatis*, which generally included grammar, rhetoric, ethics, poetry and history.[1] Finally Burke proposes his own proposition of the definition of humanism, which he places between these aforementioned extremes. In his

---

1 Paul Oskar Kristeller has recently defined humanism in this manner and stated that the other branches of knowledge besides the *studia humanitatis* were of less importance, at least for the humanist writers themselves. Kristeller 1988, 131–132: "When we reach the latter half of the fifteenth and the sixteenth century, a new phenomenon must be taken into consideration. Many scholars who had received a humanist secondary education proceeded to study other subjects at the universities or on their own, and many humanist scholars extended their interests and activities to fields other than the humanities in the strict sense of the term. Thus we find many humanists who were also philosophers, scientists, physicians and medical scholars, jurists or even theologians. It is this combination of interests that has often led to a vague or confused interpretation of Renaissance humanism and Renaissance thought and learning in general. We must distinguish between the contributions the humanists made to the humanities, which constituted their proper domain, and those they made to other branches of knowledge on account of their subsidiary scholarly interests or their amateur curiosity."

view, humanism is the movement to recover, interpret and assimilate the language, literature, learning and values of ancient Greece and Rome. Correspondingly he defines a humanist as someone who was actively involved in the movement regardless of his professional position in the society.[2]

When the relationship between humanism and science has been considered, the following words of Petrarca from the year 1368 have often been used to confirm the opinion that the Italian Renaissance humanists wholly denied the value of science.

> What is the use – I beseech you – of knowing the nature of quadrupeds, fowls, fishes, and serpents and not knowing or even neglecting man's nature, the purpose for which we are born, and whence and whereto we travel?[3]

According to Anthony Grafton, the opinion is widespread in books dealing with the Scientific Revolution and the birth of modern science.[4] In his view, however, the picture is not as simple as that. Even if the humanists had no single approach to nature or attitude towards science in general they had, as he has pointed out, a major influence in the formation of new attitudes towards nature and the study of it. Grafton argues that the humanists, in short, were not creators of a new science, but a new culture. Those who shared its values confronted the world of nature as well as that of books with a new freshness and independence – and in doing so they made the Scientific Revolution possible.[5]

---

2  Burke 1990, 2.
3  Petrarca, *On his own ignorance (De sui ipsius et multorum ignorantia)*, in *The Renaissance Philosophy of Man* 1948, 58–59, translated by Hans Nachod.
4  Anthony Grafton has summed up this attitude in the following way: "Humanism and philology seem blind alleys next to the royal road of direct study of nature, controlled experiment and quantitative natural laws that the great men of the Scientific Revolution would have to travel." Grafton 1990, 100–101. However, Grafton is partly barking up the wrong tree, because Marie Boas, for example, does not despise the term humanism the way he argues. See Boas 1962, 18–28. The attitude criticized by Grafton is more clearly apparent in Vickers 1988, 183, where he speaks of "the hostility of humanists and rhetoricians towards the sciences".
5  Grafton 1990, 103: "Italian scholars above all, notably Garin and Paolo Rossi, have emphasized that the humanists reorientated the rhetoric of natural philosophy in fundamental ways, even if they did not produce all the technical tools that scientists needed. The humanists uncovered the wide range of disagreement over means and ends that characterized ancient

In the formation of the "new culture", however, two different phases ought to be distinguished. Until the end of the fifteenth century the humanist movement was mainly a literary-oriented movement, interested in the recovery of ancient texts. The text itself was the central object of attention for these early humanists, who tried to restore the integrity of the original wording corrupted by centuries. The attitude of the next generation of humanists was different, however. These writers were no longer exclusively interested in restoring the ancient text, but sought to discover the truth about the subject matter of the texts. Thus the focus of investigation shifted from the text of an author to the need to determine the truth about nature and other similar topics.[6]

One central phase in the development was the publication of Niccolo Leoniceno's (1428–1524) *De Plinii et plurimum aliorum medicorum in medicina erroribus* (1492), in which he pointed to errors in the medical section of Pliny's *Natural History,* as well as in the works of medieval Arab physicians.[7] During the first part of the sixteenth century several classical texts covering different branches of natural philosophy were found and translated into Latin. These translations resulted in a new wave of commentaries, which in turn led to the birth of new practically orientated disciplines, like anatomy and botany, and to a revitalization of some old ones, like mechanics and poetry.[8]

---

scientific thought; they recovered ancient suggestions for alternative explanations of important phenomena; and they discovered in classical rhetoric new ways of making scientific results provocative and accessible."

6 On the changing attitude towards classical authors, see Cochrane 1976; Long 1988; Reeds 1976; and above all Nauert Jr. 1979. Also Allen G. Debus 1978, 131–134, has pointed out the complexity of Renaissance humanism in this respect.

7 Nauert Jr. 1979, 81–83. Leoniceno is also a figure central to our subject for another reason. In his *De tribus doctrinis ordinatis* Leoniceno made the first critical interpretation of the methodology presented in the beginning of Galen's *Ars parva*. Leoniceno is thus considered the father of the so-called "medical humanism" (on this see chapter 6). In his footnote Kristeller 1990, 131–132 names Leoniceno as one of his examples of humanists' "amateur curiosity" as to some matters of less importance, such as natural philosophy. It would be nice to know the grounds for this low estimation. It is worth noting, however, that Leoniceno did not write about the *studia humanitatis*, which according to Kristeller were the only proper disciplines for humanists to deal with.

8 The fact that humanists were interested in science too, can also be seen at the University of Padua. Ermolao Barbaro, a famous Venetian humanist, spent the

In this study the term humanism is not used to define the domain of the humanist disciplines, *studia humanitatis,* but to determine the humanist attitude to scientific knowledge. Above all, the attitude was practical; it had an clear emphasis on the useful.[9] Thus, in regard to the present study, the main distinction between scholastic and humanist writers does not lay in their dissimilar subject matters, but in their different definitions of arts and sciences.

## 1.2. Aristotelianism at Padua

The University of Padua, which was founded in 1222, became the centre of Aristotelian studies in the Italian peninsula in the Middle Ages and Renaissance.[10] As in other medieval Italian universities, it had three faculties: theology, jurisprudence and medicine. Abroad, the university was famous for its practical medical teaching, which drew students to Padua from every part of the continent, and even from England.[11] Perhaps ironically, Ian Hacking has described Padua as "the intellectual capital of the world".[12]

The most outstanding of all Paduan Aristotelians during the Renaissance was Jacopo Zabarella (1533–1589). For the most part

---

summer of 1484 at Padua, where he prepared a translation and commentary on Dioscorides *Materia medica.* This new kind of approach towards nature is well documented in Barbaro's writings. He wrote that he ended each day "close to eleven at night when I go down into the garden or into my neighborhood. In either place, we contemplate the herbs there and think about our Dioscorides (which no doubt we will publish soon). I use up half an hour at this. Then I go to bed." Ermolao Barbaro, *Epistolae, orationes et carmina* (2 vols; ed. V. Branca, Florence 1943), vol. 2, 61. Cited from Reeds 1976, 527; translation by Reeds.

9 Eric Cochrane speaks about "the humanistic thesis"; the thesis that "contemplation is valuable only to the extent that it arises from observation and only to the extent that it ends in action." Cochrane 1976, 1052. Perhaps Cochrane slightly exaggerates, but basically this reflects well the humanist attitude to science. See also Laird 1991, 630–631.

10 Marangon 1977, 35–37; Siraisi 1973, 16.

11 Bylebyl 1979; Schmitt 1983a, 30–31.

12 Hacking 1975, 43.

his reputation stems from his work at logic, and many scholars have examined his methodology without considering his philosophy of nature, which has often been thought to be of less importance. This is partly due to John Herman Randall's famous essay about the influence of the so-called "School of Padua" on the birth of modern science. Randall claimed that Zabarella and his predecessors at the University of Padua had developed the so-called regressus-method, which had an impact on Galileo and other pioneers of modern science.[13]

As Charles B. Schmitt has convincingly shown, however, that no unitary character of thinking among these sixteenth century writers can be found, which would justify the use of the word "school" in this context. Instead of "the School of Padua" he prefers to use the term "Venetian Aristotelianism", or "aristotelismo veneto" in Italian; in his view the term "Paduan Aristotelianism" is too narrow.[14] In his book dealing with the eclectic nature of Renaissance Aristotelianism, Schmitt has pointed out the adaptability of Italian Aristotelianism. According to him, among the very different kind of writers who have been called Aristotelians there is often only one common feature; in some way they all use Aristotle's *corpus* in their writings.[15]

Aristotelianism at Padua was by no means restricted to the realm of natural sciences. The first critical commentaries of Aristotle's *Poetics* in the sixteenth century emerged from Padua's literary academy, *Accademia degli Infiammati*, which was founded in the beginning of the 1540's. These humanistically and literary orientated commentators were equipped with a practical attitude to knowledge. Thus this group of writers ought to be counted both as humanists and Aristotelians, even if, in some respects, they differed in their orientation from more dogmatic Aristotelians, such as Zabarella. There is no need to define Aristotelians and humanists as two mutually exclusive group of scholars.

---

13  Randall 1961, The original text appeared already in 1940 as an article in the *Journal of the History of Ideas*.
14  Schmitt 1983b, 107–109. In this study the terms "Paduan" and "Venetian" Aristotelianism are used interchangeably.
15  Schmitt 1983a, 103–107. Schmitt also discusses the different forms of text used by Renaissance Aristotelians (ibid, pages 34–63).

One important feature in Venetian Aristotelianism that ought to be emphasized, is that the philosophy of Aristotle was not an isolated phenomenon. His works arrived at Padua through two different channels, each of which had an effect on the interpretation of his thought. First and foremost, during the sixteenth century the editions of the collected works of Aristotle were most often published with the commentaries of the Arab-philosopher Averroes (Ibn Rushd). The importance of this Arab transmission to the way Aristotle was understood in Italy during the sixteenth century is not always sufficiently noticed.[16] A second, perhaps less influental factor, was the influence of Aristotle's ancient Greek commentators, the most famous of whom were Alexander of Aphrodisias, Ammonius, Philoponus, Simplicius and Themistius. Jacopo Zabarella himself used both Averroes' commentaries and the ancient Greek writers when he formed his own interpretation of Aristotle's system of thought.[17]

## 1.3. The nature of arts and sciences

Inspired by Randall, the methodology of science has become the main topic of research into Venetian Aristotelianism. Various articles have been written about the methodology of Agostino Nifo, Jacopo Zabarella and other Paduan writers. Most of these articles see the methodology of science as a separate problem, however, which has little or even nothing to do with other branches of philosophy, such as metaphysics or the philosophy of nature. The nature of past research has failed to consider the methodology of science alongside other human intellectual endeavour; a fact which hardly reflects the intention of these Renaissance writers.

The starting point of this study is to examine Zabarella's logical and methodological writings within the wider context of his

---

16 The so-called Giunta-editions, which were printed at Venice, offered besides the works of Aristotle himself Averroes' commentaries to most of his writings. On the Giunta-editions, see Cranz 1976; Lucchetta 1979 and Schmitt 1979.

17 On these Neoplatonist commentators in general, see *Aristotle transformed* 1990, especially the first article by Richard Sorabji 1990. On their influence during the Renaissance, see Mahoney 1982b and Schmitt 1982.

philosophical thinking. Recent studies have considered his work either as the culmination of Renaissance Aristotelianism, or as the precursor of modern science. Neither of these approaches to Zabarella has brought in light those questions on which his writings were grounded. At the beginning of his collected logical works, *Opera logica* (1578), he drews a distinction between the eternal world of nature and the human world, which is contingent upon human volition. From this distinction he defines two corresponding kinds of knowledge, and two different methods of producing them. One purpose of this study is to show how and why Zabarella, unlike humanists, consistently prefers theoretical knowledge to its practical applications. Only in the last few years research has emphasized the importance of the relationship between Aristotelianism and humanism.[18] As a result, there exists no competent study of Zabarella's involvement with humanism. Humanist tendencies, however, were strong at Padua, and Zabarella's philosophy can be seen as a theoretical response to their practical challenge. In short, my approach tries to locate Zabarella's position within the Paduan intellectual climate.[19]

It is important to keep in mind that the meaning of the word

---

18  See for example the articles of Kessler 1990 and Schmitt 1988. Also Charles Trinkaus states in his recent review article that the relationship between philosophy and humanism is not dealt with very profoundly in *The Cambridge History of Renaissance Philosophy* 1988 or in the three volumes of *Renaissance Humanism* 1988. See Trinkaus 1990, 681–682.

19  Zabarella's methodological positions also raise the question of his relationship to Ramism. As is well-known, Ramism was the alternative logical and methodological tradition to Aristotelianism during the sixteenth century. (On Ramus' methodology in general, see Bruyère 1984 and Ong 1958.) A general study on the relationship between Ramists and Italian Aristotelians is still lacking, as only a few articles on the subject exist. Ashworth 1974, 15–16, has pointed out that, in terms of the profundity of their logical and methodological thinking, Ramists cannot be compared with Aristotelians. William Edwards 1960, 63,337–339, has also pointed out that the Paduan writers do not refer to Ramus' texts which leads him to suspect, whether they were even known to the Aristotelians. However, Cesare Vasoli 1985, xiv–xv, has maintained that although Aristotelian writers, such as Zabarella, do not explicitly refer to any of Ramus' writings, it is impossible to imagine that they were not aware of his thoughts. From my point of view it is hard to imagine that the Paduan Aristotelians were not acquainted at all with Ramus' philosophy. However, Ramism did not gain a foothold in the bastion of Paduan Aristotelianism, and the interests of the two schools of thought remained quite different. Ramists were not even considered as rivals and thus the Aristotelians felt no need to criticize their writings.

"art" (*ars*) used in this study is different from the modern use of the word in English. As Paul Oskar Kristeller has shown, the earlier meaning of the term "art" is much broader than the contemporary term "fine arts". The term originally applied to all kinds of human activities which nowadays we would call crafts or sciences. According to Kristeller, the modern idea of fine arts does not appear in Italy before the second half of the eighteenth century.[20] A. J. Close has defined the classical use of *ars* "as any rationally organized activity which has a practical rather than a speculative end (e.g. rhetoric, carpentry, politics, painting, drama), and as the system of theoretical knowledge or the intellectual expertise or the technical proficiency which such activities presuppose."[21] Even if some theoretical foreknowledge is an necessary prerequisite of successful practicing of the arts, their end, as distinct from the speculative sciences, is practical.

The topic of the second chapter of this thesis is the distinction between theoretical and practical disciplines in the Aristotelian tradition. Most of the Renaissance Aristotelians considered Aristotle almost as a contemporary, and an understanding of his position in many matters is crucial to an understanding of these later writers. At the same time interesting observations can be made about the way Aristotle was interpreted in Renaissance Italy. Zabarella's view of the hierarchy of different disciplines is studied therefore against this Aristotelian background. The other main topic is the relationship between the theoretical sciences themselves, above all between the philosophy of nature and metaphysics. At the end of the second chapter it becomes clear how Zabarella thought philosophy of nature to be a perfect science; if not in practice, at least in theory.

The third chapter deals with Zabarella's concept of logic, which further illuminates his theoretical concept of science. An interesting feature is his definition of logic chiefly as an instrument for the theoretical sciences. This distinction differentiates him from many of his contemporaries, most of which saw logic either as a science or at least an instrument for all disciplines, not just sciences. Moreover, his argument on the nature of rhetoric, poetry

---

20  Kristeller 1951, 521.
21  Close A. J. 1969, 467.

and history reveals something of his relationship to the humanist tradition.

The ontological division between art and nature also had implications for methodology, which forms the subject of the fourth chapter. Modern research on Paduan Aristotelianism has mainly been interested in the demonstrative methods of science and has considered the orders of presentation to be of minor importance. If, however, we share Zabarella's opinion, that the Aristotelian system of science was a perfect model, where the task of a scientist above all is to correct the mistakes and to place the lacking pieces to this formally or theoretically complete model, the importance of these "orders" in regard to the "methods" is worth of a fresh consideration. Zabarella's treatment of induction and the regress-method show, how he was convinced of our capacity to achieve necessary truths in science.

In the fifth chapter the concepts of art (*ars*) and nature (*natura*) are studied first in the Aristotelian tradition and then in Zabarella's thought. In the second book of the *Physics* Aristotle divided all existing things into natural beings and human artefacts, the latter of which imitate the models and methods of natural production. In the Renaissance, however, a question was raised, if an art could ever exceed the achievements of nature. Mechanics became a discipline, which formed the boundary between natural and artificial motion. During the whole of the sixteenth-century there were attempts in the commentaries on the pseudo-Aristotelian *Mechanics* to define mechanics as a speculative science, while during the Middle Ages it had been classified as one of the lower mechanical or sellularian arts.[22]

The University of Padua was famous for its medical studies, and during the sixteenth century remarkable strides were made in anatomy and other fields of medicine.[23] The subject of the sixth chapter is the practical challenge offered by medical humanists. By "practical challenge" I mean the attempt of these commentators on

---

22  As Paolo Rossi 1970 has shown, the superiority of the theoretical sciences was not in the first place called into question by the universities, but by different kinds of artificers who were keen on practising the mechanical arts. This study traces similar features in those commentaries which were used at the University of Padua.

23  Bylebyl 1979; 1985, 31–34.

medical texts to reverse the hierarchy of disciplines, so that anatomy and other parts of medicine might be considered a science instead of productive art; or at least that the arts might be considered as valuable as the sciences. For Aristotle, however, medicine was not a proper science but only an art or a technical skill. Following their master, Renaissance Aristotelians placed the art of medicine quite low in the hierarchy of arts and sciences, in spite of the successful developments in medicine at Padua. On the other hand many anatomical and medical writers claimed the status of science for their discipline. The tension between medical and philosophical writers is important for understanding Zabarella's philosophical position.

## 1.4. Jacopo Zabarella: his life and works

Jacopo Zabarella was born into a noble Paduan family on the fifth of september in 1533 and he died in the same city on 25th october, 1589, at the age of fifty-six.[24] Zabarella studied at the University of Padua and gained his doctoral degree in 1553. There is no exact information about Zabarella's subsequent activities until 1564, when he took the first chair of logic at the University of Padua. Indeed his entire teaching career was spent at his native university. In 1569 he moved to the second chair of the extraordinary professor in natural history and in 1577 to the first chair. In 1585 he moved to the second chair in natural history, as an ordinary professor, and held this chair until his death in 1589. This was in fact the highest position which Zabarella could reach in natural history at the University of Padua, because the statutes

---

24  More details on Zabarella's life can be found in Edwards 1960, first chapter (pp. 1–81). Two monographs on Zabarella's philosophy have been published. William Edwards 1960 concentrates in his Ph.D. thesis on Zabarella's logic and methodology and, in my view, follows too blindly Randall's idea of Zabarella as the forerunner of modern science. Antonino Poppi 1972 has published a wider introduction to Zabarella's thought, but fails to set him within the intellectual milieu of sixteenth-century Padua. In Lohr 1982, 233–242, there is an extensive bibliography of Zabarella's works, both manuscripts and printed versions, and also of secondary literature dealing with Zabarella.

of the university prevented native Paduans from taking the first ordinary chairs. As Jerome Bylebyl has supposed the probable purpose of this rule was to achieve a balance between local and imported talent so that the University of Padua was continually infused with new blood at the very head of its academic ranking.[25]

The first of Zabarella's publications was his *Opera logica*, which appeared in Venice in 1578. Zabarella had time to write this collection of logical works in 1576, during which a plague raged in Veneto sending Zabarella into the countryside with his family. Zabarella's next published work, *Tabula logicae* came out two years later and his commentary on Aristotle's *Posterior analytics (In duos Aristotelis libros Posteriores Analyticos commentarii)* appeared in 1582. *De doctrinae ordine apologia* (1584) was a reply to Fransesco Piccolomini's criticism of Zabarella's logic. The first of Zabarella's works in natural history, *De naturalis scientiae constitutione*, came out in 1586. This introduction was connected to his major opus in natural history, *De rebus naturalibus*, the first edition of which was published posthumously in 1590, and Zabarella having written the introduction only few weeks before his death. Zabarella's two sons edited his two incomplete commentaries on Aristotle's texts, which were also published posthumously: *In libros Aristotelis Physicorum commentarii* (1601) and *In tres Aristotelis libros De Anima commentarii* (1605).

Modern critical editions of Zabarella's texts are not available, but there are some facsimile reprints. The 1597 Cologne edition of *Opera logica* (including *Tabulae logicae, In duos Aristotelis libros Posterios Analyticos commentarii* and *Apologia*) was reprinted in Hildesheim in 1966. In the same year a reprint was made in Frankfurt from the 1608 Frankfurt edition of *Opera logica*. The text in these reprints is identical, however, because they were both printed from the plates of the 1594 Basel edition. In 1966 also *De rebus naturalibus* was reprinted in Frankfurt from a facsimile of the Frankfurt edition of 1607. The writings on logic, *De methodis* and *De regressu*, which are included in *Opera logica* were reprinted in Bologna in 1985, from the 1578 Venice-edition.

The world-view which was articulated in Paduan Aristotelianism was widely adopted throughout Europe in the text-books

---

25  Bylebyl 1979, 343–344.

on natural history at the beginning of the seventeenth century. Many of the scientific reformers of the seventeenth century learned their basic knowledge of Aristotelianism simply through these synopses of Aristotelian philosophy. The text-books were enormous popular at the turn of the century and were partly based on Zabarella's writings on logic and natural philosophy.[26]

The methodology of Paduan Aristotelianism was particularly popular in the protestant parts of Germany where it was used to legitimate new protestant theology. The reputation that Paduan Aristotelianism gained in protestant Germany has become well-known through Petersen's fundamental study on this subject.[27] As Petersen has shown, the publication of Zabarella's *Opera logica* at Basel in 1594 played an important role in this development. The Lutheran authors applied his distinction between theoretical and practical sciences to theology, since they considered theology to be a practical science which begins from the end or purpose of an action and seeks to discover the means by which this end could be attained.[28] However, a fundamental study of the reception of Paduan Aristotelians in Germany and England is still lacking.[29]

---

26 See Reif 1969.
27 Petersen 1921, especially pages 195–218.
28 Lohr 1988, 630. On the impact of Zabarella's logic on some of these German writers, see chapter 3.2. of the present study.
29 Schmitt 1983c has collected some facts about Zabarella's reception in England at the turn of the seventeenth century.

# 2. Arts and sciences in Zabarella's thought

## 2.1. Aristotle on arts and sciences

Like many other features of Western intellectual history, the first theoretical discussions of the words "natural" and "artificial" appeared in the works of Plato and Aristotle. There are earlier uses of these words in a scientific context, as for example in the books on Hippocratic medicine, but Plato and Aristotle were the first two writers to pay close theoretical attention to the terms and the relationship between them.[1]

In several passages in his corpus, Aristotle draws the well-known distinction between theoretical, practical and productive disciplines. He considers metaphysics, mathematics and natural philosophy to be the three theoretical sciences.[2] In the sixth book

---

1 On Hippocratic medicine see *Hippocratic Writings* 1987; Frede 1987 and Smith 1979.
2 For example in *Topics* 157a10–11, *Metaphysics* 1025–25 and 1064a10–19. There are, however, some passages in the Aristotelian corpus, where this division seems blurred. In the first chapter of the *Parts of Animals* (640a1–3) Aristotle seems to separate natural science from other theoretical disciplines and count it among productive disciplines. It seems to me, however, that Aristotle is here drawing a distinction between the different modes of necessity and demonstration required in mathematics and in natural sciences. In other words, Aristotle is not trying to say that biology is not a theoretical endeavour, but that it is different from the solely theoretical activity of mathematics. It can be said, too, that he is here using the word "theoretical" in a technical sense and not in the general way that he employs it (as in *Metaphysics* 1025b25). What is interesting, too, is that he takes the production of health as his example here, which refers more to the productive art of

of his *Nicomachean Ethics* the difference between theoretical and productive disciplines becomes quite clear. The subject matter of theoretical sciences (*episteme*) are eternal and necessary things, such as natural beings. On the other hand the subject matter of productive arts (*tekhne*) are contingent things whose essence is dependent on human volition. These disciplines have also different ends. In theoretical sciences knowledge is an internal end, but in productive sciences a product is an external end, separate from the producing process.[3]

There are some other passages in the Aristotelian corpus, however, which make this neat distinction somewhat complicated. In the first chapter of the *Metaphysics,* Aristotle is analyzing the qualities of productive crafts (*tekhne*).[4] It is obvious that here Aristotle understands the word *tekhne* in a wider sense covering both theoretical and productive sciences. His aim here is not to classify the sciences and other disciplines, but to point out the difference between *tekhne* and other lower kinds of consciousness.[5]

In the first chapter of the *Metaphysics* Aristotle states that "an art arises, when from many notions gained by experience one

---

medicine than to natural sciences. On the interpretation of this problematic passage see Boylan 1984, 136; Gotthelf 1987, 197–198; and on a more common level Grene 1985, 9–13.

3  Aristotle, *Nicomachean Ethics* 1140a1–24.
4  Aristotle, *Metaphysics* 981a13–b13.
5  Martha Nussbaum has pointed out that, at the beginning of *Metaphysics*, Aristotle distinguishes four essential criteria for a *tekhne*: universality, teachability, precision and concern with explanation. Nussbaum thinks that this wider meaning of the word *tekhne* is the basic use of the word in Aristotle's philosophy, not the one in the *Nicomachean Ethics*. The most problematic of Nussbaum's criteria for a *tekhne* is precision (*akribeia*). Nowhere in the first chapter of the first book of *Metaphysics* does Aristotle give precision as a criterion for a *tekhne*. Indeed Nussbaum's own text here refers not to Aristotle, but to former fifth-century discussions of *tekhne*. See Nussbaum 1986, 95–96. In his second chapter (982a8–b10) Aristotle does mention *akribeia* as a criterion for estimating the nobility of different sciences and ranking them in a hierarchy, but here Aristotle speaks not of *tekhne* but *episteme*. Moreover, at the beginning of his *Ethics* (1094b12–27) Aristotle says that we cannot demand the same kind of exactness from the arts and practical sciences as from the theoretical ones. As we shall see in chapter 4.4., also Zabarella discussed about the meaning of the word *akribeia*. Zabarella assumed it to be no criterion of arts, however, but only of the theoretical sciences.

universal judgment about similar objects is produced."[6] Aristotle takes medicine to be his example. We know by experience which medicine cured Callias or Socrates, but only when we have made an universal judgment of similar cases, we call medicine an art. Experience concerns individuals, and art is knowledge of universals. If a physician only has knowledge of the universal, however, he can fail to cure his patient because all actions and their results must be concerned with the individual. A physician's task is not to cure man in general, but Callias or Socrates or some other person with an individual name. Aristotle stresses that knowledge and experience belong more to art than to experience. He makes a division between artists and men of experience. The latter know that a thing is so but they do not know the reason, whereas the former group knows both. So in contrast to men of experience, artists know how to teach their art.[7]

It seems reasonable to suppose that Aristotle really uses *tekhne* in two different ways. In its wider meaning, as found at the beginning of *Metaphysics*, it means all arts and sciences as distinct from pure experience and other lower kinds of human consciousness. In *Nicomachean Ethics*, however, Aristotle intends to make a division between arts, practical and theoretical sciences. There, therefore *tekhne* refers only to the productive activities.

In Aristotle's corpus there are passages where he stresses the importance of theoretical knowledge even in the practice of crafts. Besides the aforementioned passage at the beginning of *Metaphysics*, also in the last book of *Nicomachean Ethics* Aristotle takes medicine as his example. In order to be a specialist in his field a doctor must know the universal principles of his discipline. A doctor may succeed in curing a patient by only relying on his experience but if you really want to be a professional craftsman you have to have a theoretical knowledge of your *tekhne*, too. According to Aristotle this is also true for those who intend to be legislators.[8] In the third book of *Politics*, Aristotle asks, who has the right to evaluate persons engaged in a trade. Generally speaking he shares the opinion that only colleagues equal to that person are able to make an evaluation and, in the case of medicine,

---

6  Aristotle, *Metaphysics* 981a5–7.
7  Aristotle, *Metaphysics* 981a7–b9.
8  Aristotle, *Nicomachean Ethics* 1180b13–22.

only other physicians are able to evaluate a member of their profession. He goes on to say, however, that there are three kinds of physicians: first, the ordinary practioner, secondly, the master physician and thirdly, the man educated in the art. In every art there exists this third class of professionals, who are naturally permitted to judge other members of their craft.[9]

The mentioned passages show clearly that Aristotle is willing to admit that every *tekhne* has a theoretical background as well as a practical result. He was not, however, very eager to analyze the relationship between these different parts of *tekhne*, and leaves the question as to what really is the epistemological status of the theoretical part of a *tekhne* unanswered. In what way does this part of a *tekhne* differ from the knowledge achieved in the theoretical sciences, if it differs at all? As in the theoretical sciences, the end of this part of *tekhne* is undoubtedly knowledge, not operation. The subject matter is, however, contingent upon things which fall under human volition, about which firm knowledge (*episteme*) is impossible.[10] What is certain, however, is that many Renaissance writers took the distinction between the theoretical and practical part of a *tekhne* for granted, using it, for example, to raise the low status of practical disciplines, as I shall show.

Alongside the philosophical dispute between arts and sciences there existed a conflict between these disciplines in respect of their dignity and nobility. This was a popular topic of discussion within the medieval classification of arts and sciences; a debate which continued even in Renaissance times.[11] Classical antiquity had already placed the different disciplines in a certain order; the main feature being that arts were ranked below the theoretical disciplines. There was, however, a hierarchy within the arts as well. Medicine was often seen as the most valuable and the noblest of all arts, and was almost considered equal to the theoretical sciences.[12] In the Renaissance the relationship between theoretical

---

9  Aristotle, *Politics* 1282a1–6.
10  The question comes near another one, namely, in what sense Aristotle thought ethics and politics to be sciences. In ethical and political matters the degree of necessity is lower than in the natural sciences. Aristotle seems to have thought, however, that also in ethics and politics it is possible to have scientific knowledge in the proper meaning of the term. On this matter see Hardie 1980, 28–45, 365–368; Knuuttila 1989a, 211.
11  On the medieval classifications of arts and sciences see Weisheipl 1978.
12  Ferrari and Vegetti 1983, 200–205.

natural science and medicine, which was classified in the Middle Ages as a craft, became controversial.[13]

## 2.2. Contemplative sciences and productive arts

Zabarella's collected logical works, *Opera logica*, begins with a work called *De natura logicae* (On the nature of logic). The main topic of this study is the scientific status of logical disciplines, which was a popular question in the sixteenth century. Following Aristotle, Zabarella draws a fundamental distinction at the beginning of his study between the two kinds of things that exist.[14] Some things are necessary and eternal; others are contingent, that is they can exist or not. The necessary things have either always been and were made by nobody, or if they were made, they were made by nature operating on necessary causes. As singular beings they are not eternal, but can always be reduced to universality and so can be considered dependent on necessary causes. According to Zabarella all natural beings belong to this first class, which is independent of human will. The other category contains all those things which are dependent on human volition, about the existence of which we have the power to choose. They are never necessary, only contingent and arbitrary, because their existence depends wholly on our will.[15]

---

13 I shall return to this problem in chapter 6. On the medieval classification and status of crafts, see Alessio 1965 and Ovitt Jr. 1983.

14 The relevant passage is *Nicomachean Ethics* 1139b18–24.

15 Zabarella 1597, 2a–b: "Res omnes in duo genera dividuntur ab Aristotele in 3.cap. 6.libri de Moribus ad Nicomachum. Alias enim necessarias, ac sempiternas esse dicit, alias contingentes, quae esse et non esse possunt. Necessarias quidem vocat tum eas omnes, quae ipsae per se semper sunt et nunquam fiunt; tum eas, quae fiunt quidem, non tamen a voluntate nostra, sed a natura per certas causas operante. Hae namque etsi quatenus sunt singulares, non semper sunt, tamen quatenus ad universitatem rediguntur et ita a certis causis necessario pendere considerantur; ut eas esse, vel non esse, fieri aut non fieri, non sit in nostra voluntate constitutum, eatenus necessarie ac sempiternae dici possunt, cuiusmodi esse res omnes naturales manifestum est. Restat ut alterum divisionis membrum res illas contineat, quae ab hominis voluntate pendent, quoniam eas facere, vel non facere, in arbitrio nostro

Zabarella also distinguishes two categories of discipline: one involves those things which are dependent on our will; the other includes things which are dependent on the causes that are above our volition. According to him, there are no other disciplines, because all things fall into these two classes.[16] Further, these two classes of discipline have different functions and ends, which can be deduced from the very nature of that which they contain. That which cannot be made, can be contemplated, and thus is certainly known. Those things which can be made, require thought before they can be created. The main purpose of this latter group is not knowledge but production; yet, without knowledge production is either impossible; or at least more difficult, and the resultant products worse. Zabarella thinks that Aristotle is correct about moral disciplines when, in the first book of *Nicomachean Ethics*, he says that their end is not knowledge but action.[17]

Having made this primary distinction, Zabarella deals with disciplines concerning necessary things. Because science can be reached only by contemplation, he calls these contemplative sciences (*scientiae contemplativae*). He divides these contemplative sciences into three kinds: divine science, which is also called metaphysics; mathematics; and natural science. Metaphysics considers things which are separated from matter; natural philosophy looks at material things as material; and mathematics explores those material things which are not entirely without

---

positum est. Quocirca nullam habent necessitatem, sed contingentes dicuntur, quae tum esse, tum non esse nostro arbitratu possunt."

16 Zabarella 1597, 2d: "Quoniam igitur disciplinam omnem, quae aliquid doceat, rem aliquam tractare necesse est, duo oriuntur disciplinarum genera; quorum unum in iis rebus versatur, quae a nobis fieri possunt; alterum in iis, quae non a nobis fiunt, sed vel semper sunt, vel certas alias causas extra nostram voluntatem positas consequuntur. Aliud equidem disciplinae genus non video. Nam si quae alia praeter has statuatur, ea, quum nihil tractet, profecto nihil erit."

17 Zabarella 1597, 3a–c: "Duo hi diversi fines ex ipsa rerum natura deducuntur. Nam res illas, quas efficere non possumus, eo tantum consilio contemplamur, ut eas cognoscamus, non ut efficiamus … Eas vero, quas facere possumus, ideo consideramus, ut efficiamus. Quod si earum quoque cognitionem quarere videamur, scopus tamen praecipuus non est cognitio, sed operatio. Nam ea mente quaerimus cognoscere, ut per cognitionem efficere aliquid valeamus, quod sine cognitione aut non efficeremus, aut difficilius, vel deterius efficeremus. Propterea de morali disciplina loquens recte dicebat Aristoteles in 3.cap. 1.lib. de Moribus, finem ipsius non cognitionem esse, sed actionem." Zabarella refers to *Nicomachean Ethics* 1095a5–6.

matter. However, their essence is not dependent on sense perception, from which they are distinguished with mental consideration. According to Zabarella there are no other sciences, since all the other disciplines dealing with contingent things are dependent on human will. Strictly speaking, there are two reasons, why all the other disciplines cannot be called sciences at all. First, knowing is not their end, and secondly, they gain knowledge only of contingent, not necessary things.[18]

Continuing his reference to Aristotle, Zabarella distinguishes five different intellectual habits. First he mentions science (*scientia*), which Aristotle defined both in the *Nicomachean ethics* and in the *Posterior Analytics*. Zabarella notes that Aristotle requires two kinds of certainty from science. One is in the knowable things, which are necessary *simpliciter*, and the other is in the mind of the scientist, who must be certain that the things cannot be otherwise. We cannot have a knowledge of contingent things or even of necessary ones, unless our mind is sure that the things cannot be different.[19] It is important to notice that Zabarella demands this twofold necessity from the theoretical sciences. For

---

18 Zabarella 1597, 3c–f: "Haec quum ita se habeant, disciplinae illae, quae in rebus necessariis versantur eo tantum scopo, ut eas cognoscant, merito Scientiae contemplativae appellatae sunt ... Satis est in praesentia, tres esse ad summum scientias contemplativas: divinam, quae Metaphysica dicitur, mathematicam et naturalem. Divina quidem res a materia penitus abiunctas considerat; naturalis autem res materiales, quatenus materiales sunt; mathematica vero eas, quae materiales quidem sunt, propterea quod fine materia non existerent; tamen quia earum essentia a sensili materia non pendet, ab ea per mentalem considerationem separantur. Si aliud genus rerum, quae a nostra voluntate non pendeant, praeter haec tria non datur, sequitur neque scientiam aliam dari, praeter eas tres, quas modo nominavimus. Reliquae omnes disciplinae in rebus illis versantes, quae quod ab humana voluntate aeque fieri, ac non fieri possunt, Contingentes ab Aristotele vocantur; si proprie loqui velimus, scientiae appellandae non sunt, tum quod cognitionem pro fine non habent, quemadmodum diximus; tum etiam quod ea cognitio, quum rerum necessarium non sit, scientia nominari non debet."

19 Zabarella 1597, 4a–b: "Docet autem ... Aristoteles, duplicem in scientia requiri necessitatem; unam in ipsa re scita, quae simpliciter necessaria sit et aliter ese non possit; alteram in animo scientis, qui omnino certus esse debet, rem illam aliter esse non posse. Harum duarum conditionum altera utravis sublata non habemus scientiam, ut si rerum contingentium nostra cognitio sit, vel necessarium quidem, sed cum animi incertitudine et haesitatione." The Aristotelian passages referred to are *Nicomachean Ethics* 1139b23–35 and *Posterior Analytics* 71b9–16.

him it is not enough that syllogistical demonstrations concerning the subjects dealt with in the theoretical sciences are necessary, for he says that the subjects themselves must be unchanging and necessary.

Zabarella further divides contingent things into two groups. One is action, which is directed towards good or bad; the intellectual habit of the moral disciplines is called prudence (*prudentia*). The other is production, which when it is directed towards operative material, is called art (*ars*). Prudence is a habit directed towards action according to right reason (*habitum recta cum ratione activum*), and art is a habit directed towards production according to right reason (*habitum cum recta ratione effectivum*).[20] The difference between action and operation can be imagined in terms of the relationship between a master and his servant. Like servants, all arts exist to serve people's ultimate happiness. Our civil life benefits from the products we make. In action, however, happiness consists in the virtue of the action itself, not in its end product. Action is like the master whose virtuous action is served by production.[21] As we shall see later, in Zabarella's view, the happiness gained by action can never compare with that ultimate happiness which is achieved by contemplation alone.

Besides science, prudence and art, Aristotle mentions two other

---

20 Zabarella 1597, 4b–c: "Rerum autem contingentium et a nostra voluntate pendentium duo sunt genera, ut Aristoteles docet in 4.capite 6.libri de Moribus, unde duo quoque disciplinarum in his versantium classes oriuntur. Eorum enim, quae a nobis fiunt, alia agi, alia effici proprie dicuntur. Actio quidem eorum est, quae ad virtutem et vitium pertinent, quorum intellectualis habitus prudentia dicitur, atque in his tota moralis disciplina versatur. Effectio vero eorum, quae ad materialia opera pertinent, quorum habitus intellectualis dicitur ars. Propterea prudentiam et artem definiens Aristoteles, dicit prudentiam esse habitum recta cum ratione activum, artem vero habitum cum recta ratione effectivum."

21 Zabarella 1597, 4d–e: "Inter actionem et effectionem illud discrimen est, quod inter finem et ea, quae sunt ante finem, seu modo quodam, quod inter dominum et servum. Artes enim omnes aliquam materiam tractantes et elaborantes, ad civilem felicitatem, tanquam eius ministrae diriguntur, siquidem ab illis omnibus vitae civili commoda suppeditantur, proinde nihil propter se efficiunt, sed propter felicitatem. Actio vero non ad felicitatem dirigitur, sed felicitas ipsa est apud Aristotelem, qui felicitatem vult esse non virtutem ipsam, sed actionem ex habitu virtutis proficiscentem. Huiusmodi actionem igitur actio domina est et finis omnium effectionum. Effectiones autem omnes propter actionem, tanquam propter finem et ipsius servae ac ministrae sunt.

habits in *Nicomachean Ethics:* intuitive reason (*intellectus*) and wisdom (*sapientia*). With intuitive reason we grasp the principles of science, so it is even more certain and necessary than science. The highest habit of all, wisdom, combines the intellect with science. There are, therefore, five intellectual habits of which three are necessary and eternal; that is science, intuitive reason and wisdom, and two contingent; or dependent on our free will, that is prudence and art.[22]

In defining the nature of logic it is the difference between art and science which has caused most confusion according to Zabarella. He considers that in *Posterior Analytics* and in *Nicomachean Ethics* Aristotle sought to point out the essential difference between these two kinds of discipline. In the latter treatise Aristotle compared production with generation of natural beings. He said that every art is practiced in generation; not in generation of natural beings, but in man-made objects such as beds, ships or houses. It is this form of generation and production which art teaches by means of the right producing habit.[23]

---

22  Zabarella 1597, 4f–5a: "Tres quidem intellectuales habitus ex iis, quae dicta sunt, colligimus: scientiam, prudentiam et artem. Sed alios duos adiicit Aristoteles in 6.lib. de Moribus, intellectum et sapientiam. Intellectus quidem dicitur principiorum cognitio, ex qua scientiam conclusionum adipiscimur, quare maiorem habet certitudinem et necessitatem, quam scientia, ut probat Aristoteles in 2.cap. 1.libri posteriorum Analyticorum et in ultimo capite 2.libri. Sapientia vero est habitus praestantissimus, scientiam cum intellectu coniungens et veluti scientia caput habens, ut in illo 6.lib. de Moribus docet Aristoteles. Quum igitur quinque sint habitus intellectuales, manifestum est tres ita esse rerum simpliciter necessarium et aeternatum, ut extra eas nullum locum habeant, nempe scientiam, intellectum et sapientiam; duos vero contingentium, quae in nostrae voluntatis arbitrio sunt constitutae, prudentiam et artem."

23  Zabarella 1597, 5c–d: "Propterea etiam in quarto capite sexti libri de Moribus inquit Aristoteles, artem omnem in generationem versari, non quidem generationem intelligens naturalem, sed eam, quae a nobis fit per habitum artis, ut generationem lecti, navis, domus et similium. Haec enim et alia eiusmodi, quae nondum sunt, docet ars cum recta ratione generare et efficere." The relevant passages are *Posterior Analytics* 100a8–9 and *Nicomachean Ethics* 1140a1–23. I shall return to the comparison of natural beings with man-made artefacts in the fifth chapter.

## 2.3. The primacy of theoretical sciences

According to Zabarella there are different meanings of the word science (*scientia*). In the widest sense it includes all knowledge. In this sense all practical and productive disciplines can be called sciences. On this ground medicine has also been called science.[24] Like science, the word art (*ars*) can refer to more than the productive disciplines; that is to active and contemplative philosophy as well. Averroes used the term in this way when he spoke about the speculative arts.

Zabarella, however, wants to use the terms "art" and "science" more restrictively. The use of the word *ars* is widest when it is extended even to the contemplative sciences, but less wide and less inaccurate when it covers all the disciplines except the contemplative ones. According to him, the use of *ars* is, however, most precise when it coincides only with the productive arts, as Aristotle accepted and defined the word in the fourth chapter of the sixth book of the *Nicomachean Ethics*.[25] Undoubtedly Zabarella himself preferred the definition of *ars* which Aristotle had used in his *Ethics*, to the one used in the *Metaphysics*. In this Zabarella emphasizes the hierarchical nature of the division between different disciplines; the whole of active philosophy aiming ultimately at the higher sphere of contemplation.

> Without any disputation it is clear that active happiness both in Plato and Aristotle is not the ultimate end of a human being. That is contemplation, which is the human's best end and the sum of all his perfection.[26]

24 Zabarella 1597, 17e: "Dum enim scientiae nomen late sumitur pro omni cognitione, quaecunque ea sit, non modo logica, sed et activa philosophia et ars omnis docens potest vocari scientia, propterea quia cognitionem aliquam tradit. Hac ratione medicina solet quandoque appellari scientia."

25 Zabarella 1597, 17f–18a: "Propterea latissima est huius vocis significatio, quando ad contemplativas quoque scientias extenditur; minus autem lata et minus impropria, quando solis exceptis contemplativis, alias omnes disciplinas complectitur; sed maxime propria, quando per solis effectricibus artibus sumitur, quo modo nomen artis accepit ac definivit Aristoteles in 4.cap. 6.lib. de Moribus."

26 Zabarella 1597, 97b: "Sed sine ulla altercatione constituendum nobis est, activam felicitatem tum apud Aristotelem, tum apud Platonem non esse ultimum hominis finem, sed contemplativam, quae praestantissimus finis hominis est ac summa eius perfectio."

The function of active philosophy is to remove hindrance to knowledge. Contemplative philosophy is the ultimate end and master of all active philosophy.

The difference between arts and sciences becomes clearer, when Zabarella discusses the subject matter and the ends of different disciplines. He distinguishes four different meanings of the word subject matter (*subiectum*) in various disciplines. First, it is possible to speak about the subject matter of some science or art and mean all the things that are treated in this discipline. This is the widest use of the term and includes all principles and affections. For example, in the art of medicine the human body, health, disease, remedies, medicine and symptoms can all be called subject matter.

There can, however, be some certain qualifications concerning the subject matter of a discipline. Thus the speculative sciences can be distinguished from the operative disciplines by claiming that the subject matter of speculative sciences must be necessary beings and their names and existence must be known to us. The subject matter of speculative sciences must therefore have proper principles, and affections that can be demonstrated through the principles.

Thirdly, Zabarella speaks about the subject matter of the operative disciplines. In these disciplines the end, metaphorically speaking, can be called subject matter; such as health which is the ultimate end of medicine. According to Zabarella, a science is formed through its subject matter, but an art through its end. However, even arts have a proper subject matter which is separated from their end, such as the human body in the art of medicine. Thus the human body is the subject matter of medicine and health its end. The human being is also the subject matter of moral philosophy; but it is his mental, not physical health, which is important. The ends of moral philosophy are virtues and virtuous action of which happiness is constituted.

There are some arts which have both an internal and an external end, in Zabarella's view. For example in the art of building the house itself is an internal end, but living and storing the furniture are external ends. There are arts, too, whose end is wholly in the action itself, like the art of navigation. The art of medicine has only one proper end; that of producing health. It serves no other, external purpose. On the other hand, it can be said that no art is

31

wholly self-centred, for all serve some other external end, which, ultimately, can be termed happiness. In the case of medicine, therefore, health increases happiness.[27]

Fourthly, according to Zabarella, the proper subject matter of productive disciplines can be separately defined; as the human body in the art of medicine or, in moral discipline, the human mind. As we have already seen, distinctions can be made as to the degree of knowledge demanded by different disciplines. In the contemplative sciences, the proper task of a scientist is to know his propositions thoroughly. In Zabarella's view, a contemplative philosopher wants to know all things that are worth knowing. Contemplation itself brings about an understanding of all things, not only in themselves, but in all the ways they can be known, so that there is nothing left for the other disciplines to know.[28]

The subject matter of the contemplative sciences is proper. It cannot correspond to the subject matter of any other discipline. In the productive disciplines, however, the subject matter can be common; for example the human body is not only the subject matter of medicine, but of other arts too, and even forms part of the subject matter of natural philosophy. So in Zabarella's view the contemplative sciences differ from each other according to their subject matter, but the productive arts according to their ends. The subject matter of every science has two parts: the matter that is called the topics under consideration (*res considerata*) and the form, which is called the mode of consideration (*modus considerandi*). The topics under consideration can be common with other disciplines, but the mode of consideration is separately related to each science, and binds in common the topics under consideration.[29] So even if natural philosophy and medicine share the same subject matter, they can always be separated according to

---

27  Zabarella 1597, 34d–36d.
28  Zabarella 1597, 48b: "Philosophus enim contemplativus rerum omnium, quae dignae cognitu sint, notitiam assequi vult. Ideo ipsius contemplationi res omnes subiiciuntur; nec solum dico res omnes, sed et omnibus modis, quibus cognosci possunt, ut aliis disciplinis nulla res cognoscenda relinquatur."
29  Zabarella 1597, 39d–e: "Nam subiectum scientiae duas partes habet. Unam veluti materiam, quae dicitur res considerata; alterum veluti formam, quae dicitur ratio et modus considerandi. Res quidem considerata non est cuiusque scientiae propria, sed potest ei cum aliis esse communis. Modus autem considerandi cuique proprius est et rem consideratam restringit, quae ipsa per se communis erat."

1

their different ways of treating that matter, and their different ends.[30] Zabarella neatly sums up his classification of the different meanings of the word subject:

> From all that has been said, we can define four meanings of the word subject. Firstly, understood in its widest sense, it refers to whatever is under consideration in any discipline. Secondly, it can be understood as the subject of demonstration in the contemplative sciences. Thirdly, the end can metaphorically be accepted as the subject in operative disciplines, just as health is said to be the subject of medicine. Fourthly, it can be the subject matter of an operation, which is the proper subject in operative disciplines, just as the human body in the art of medicine, or iron in fabrication.[31]

In productive disciplines it is not necessary to define the things under production as strictly as in the contemplative sciences. The reason for this is that the productive arts do not aim at knowledge, and the knowledge they need is not complete. In *De methodis* Zabarella makes a division between incomplete (*confusa*) and complete (*distincta*) knowledge. Further, the complete knowledge can be absolutely complete (*simpliciter*), or complete only in proportion to the nature of the discipline. For example a natural scientist must have an absolutely complete knowledge of all metals, but the blacksmith need only have enough knowledge of a metal to enable him to carry out his profession. The blacksmith's knowledge of metals is not absolutely complete, but it is sufficiently complete for his discipline. Thus it is enough for a blacksmith to know iron well enough to make a sword out of it.[32]

---

30 On this subject also Edwards 1960, 108–109, where he points out, that the distinction between *res considerata* and *modus considerandi* was already apparent in Angelo Tio's work. On the relationship between natural philosophy and medicine see chapter 6.4.

31 Zabarella 1597, 40c–d: "Ex omnibus, quae dicta sunt, quatuor subiecti acceptiones colligimus. Prima est, quando subiectum latissime sumitur pro quacunque re considerata in quavis disciplina. Secunda, quando sumitur pro subiecto demonstrationis, quale habent scientiae contemplativae. Tertia, quando per metaphoram accipitur subiectum pro fine facultatis operatricis, ut quum subiectum medicinae dicimus esse sanitatem. Quarta demum, quando sumitur pro subiecto operationis, quod in operatricibus proprie subiectum dicitur, ut in arte medica corpus humanum et in fabrili ferrum."

32 Zabarella 1597, 38d–39b, 148a–c.

Correspondingly the moral philosopher has to know the mind and the parts of it, but not completely; and the doctor has to know only enough about the eye in order to cure it. Since Zabarella considers a moral philosopher to be, in some respects, a mental physician, he must also have some knowledge of the human mind.[33]

In his collected works on natural philosophy Zabarella makes an interesting division between the arts involved in the process of building a ship. The art which produces the raw materials for a ship is the most useful, but nobody would call it architecture or a high art. That art which builds the ship out of this material, is termed architecture, and is highly respected, because the architect defines the ultimate appearance of the ship.[34] The situation is similar in building a house. That art which produces the material is the lowest one; the art of building is more highly respected than the first, but the noblest of all arts is that, which do not participate in, but precedes the building process by designing the house. Architects do not participate in practical action but, in assigning the tasks to each individual art, their work is an universal action.[35] According to Zabarella, therefore, the noblest arts are the most theoretical of all, not the most useful ones.

In summary, Zabarella wants to point out the basic difference between art and science. Science considers what exists already, but art considers generation. The subject matter of a science is that

---

33  Zabarella 1597, 50a–c.
34  Zabarella; *De rebus naturalibus* 1590, 672c–d: "Nam ars illa, quae navibus construendis solam materiam subministrat, utilissima est, eamque nemo architectonicam, seu artem principem appellaret. Ars illa, quae ex illa materia navim extruit, potest architectonica nominari et adhuc magis alia superior ars, quae huic praecipit quomodo et qualem efficere navim debeat."
35  Zabarella 1590, 672d–e: "Ita ars illa, quae domibus aedificandis materiam suppeditat, ignobilis est, nec potest vocari princeps. Ars autem aedificandi, quae domum efficit, magis potest appellari ars princeps, quoniam illi imperat. Sed multo magis ars alia, quae non facit, sed facienti praecipit, nomine architectonicae dignanda est et hos solemus vocare architectos, quoniam officium principis est non occupari in aliqua actione particulari, sed in aliqua tantum universali, qua singulis ministris propria officia distribuantur, ac principis auctoritas et agendi facultas communicetur." In stressing the theoretical part of every art Zabarella follows Aristotle, who in the beginning of his *Metaphysics* says that the master-workers of each craft are wiser, more honourable and know in a truer sense than the manual workers, because the former know the causes of that which is done. See Aristotle, *Metaphysics* 981a30–b2. Also at the beginning of the *Nicomachean Ethics* (1094a7–18) he notes that arts can be placed in a hierarchy according to their ends.

which is necessarily, but the subject matter of an art is the production of things which do not yet exist but which can be made by man. The contemplative philosopher does not want to produce anything, but rather wants to know and arrange the forms of existing, eternal things. The artist wants to produce something that does not already exist. There is, however, another basic difference between arts and sciences; namely their ends. The end of the contemplative sciences is knowledge for its own sake, but in the productive arts the end is an actual product. In moral disciplines the ultimate end is human happiness, but in operative arts the end is the result of the production process, and is separate from the process itself.

## 2.4. Putting sciences in order

One topic that was very popular in the Renaissance discussions of the sciences was the criteria for the hierarchy of disciplines. In fifteenth-century Florence the famous dispute arose as to the greater nobility of jurisprudence or medicine.[36] At the end of the century Nicoletto Vernia took part in the same academic discussion in Padua.[37] The discussion involved other popular topics of academic debate, like the meaning and priority of active versus contemplative life. Among the writings of the Paduan Aristotelians are several examples of how vital these themes remained, even in the sixteenth century.[38]

The most important of these debates for our present subject are the criteria for arranging sciences and other disciplines in a hierarchical order. Some passages in Aristotle's *On the soul* and

36  On this dispute, see the foreword of Eugenio Garin in *La disputa delle arti nel Quattrocento* 1947, XIII–XVIII.
37  Vernia, Nicoletto, *"Quaestio est, an medicina nibilior atque praestantior sit iure civili."* (1486). In *La disputa ...* 1947, 111–123. On Vernia's opinion about the nature of medical knowledge see chapter 6.2. On Vernia in general, see Nardi 1958, 95–126; Pagallo 1983, 813–842, and CHRP 1988, 839.
38  On the discussion of active and contemplative life in sixteenth century at the University of Padua, see Poppi 1988. See also Thorndike 1936, 185–190 for later sixteenth-century discussions on the topic.

*Posterior analytics* were the basic sources for this classification.[39] In these passages Aristotle distinguishes two criteria for comparing the sciences: the nobility or necessity of their subject matter; and the kind of demonstration being used.

In line with Aristotle's *Posterior Analytics,* Zabarella distinguishes three different instances, when a science can be called exactior or prior to another. In the first criterion of priority he compares resolution with demonstration *propter quid.* It is better to know the cause of something by means of *demonstratio propter quid,* than to have a knowledge of its mere essence by means of resolution.[40] The second criterion of priority is based on the subject matter of the science. Those sciences which deal with things separated from perceptible matter are more exact than and prior to the sciences which deal with perceptible things. For example, of the subalternative sciences of arithmetic and music, arithmetic is more exact and prior because it treats numbers separated from matter. In the same way metaphysics is more exact than, and prior to, the philosophy of nature. The third criterion of priority relates to the premises of sciences. Those sciences that are dependent on fewer premises are more exact and prior in Zabarella's view. Thus arithmetic is more exact than geometry, because in arithmetic unity and number are simpler than point and magnitude in geometry. In this way metaphysics can be considered a more exact science than natural sciences, because they are dependent on it. The natural world cannot be known perfectly without a knowledge of divine things.[41]

In the posthumous commentary of Aristotle's *On the soul* (*De anima*), Zabarella repeats his first two criteria for priority; the priority of causal knowledge and the necessity of the subject matter. However, here he entertains the possibility that these criteria might in some cases be contradictory. For example astrology has a nobler subject matter than geometry, but is less noble in respect of its causality. This then leads Zabarella to ask which criteria should be given preference.

Many have answered the question by saying that the nobility of

---

39  Aristotle, *De anima* 402a1–4; *Analytica posteriora* 87a30ff.
40  For a more detailed consideration of the resolutive and the compositive method see chapter 4.2.
41  Zabarella 1597, 981c–983d.

subject matter should be given priority, because only in that can absolute primacy be discussed. According to Zabarella, however, the question is not as simple as that. In most cases the science with a nobler subject can be considered prior, but not always. All human knowledge can be compared, and there are no grounds for giving either of these criteria absolute priority. Besides subjects considered in the sciences, there are other phenomena that are infinite, or are at least beyond all human comparison. Such a phenomenon is God; and even an incomplete consideration of God is more valuable than an exact consideration of other things.[42] Following Aristotle's *On the parts of animals*, Zabarella suggests in *De methodis* that in the contemplative sciences, the nobility of subject matter should be considered prior to the causality of knowledge. Yet in logic, where the instruments of science are considered, the nobler instrument is the one which is more exact and produces more certain knowledge. In this respect the demonstrative method is nobler than the resolutive one. It produces more exact knowledge; that is, knowledge of the causes of obscure things.[43]

For Zabarella it was a moot point whether all sciences could be arranged in a strict hierarchy. He took for granted the primacy of the contemplative sciences over the productive arts and practical disciplines but, in his opinion, there were no simple criteria for making a hierarchical division within the theoretical sciences. He concludes that sometimes the principal factor is the necessity of the subject matter, and sometimes it is the knowledge of the causes of things compared with the knowledge of the mere essence of those things.

Zabarella distinguishes the principles common to all sciences (*principia communia*) from the principles that are characteristic to each science (*principia propria*). The common principles are not

42 Zabarella, *In tres libros De anima commentarii* 1605, 2rB–2vB: "Melius itaque est, ut ad propositam quaestionem dicamus, contingere interdum, ut absolute nobilior dicatur illa scientia, quae est de re nobiliore; interdum est evenire, ut illa, quae certior, atque exquisitior est, dicatur absolute praestantior, licet subiecti nobilitate vincatur. Magis tamen, ac saepius contingere, ut praestantior dicatur scientia a subiecto, quam a certitudine, etsi non semper. Ratio huius rei est, quoniam omnis humana cognitio cum omni humana cognitione comparabilis est, nec datur tantus certitudinis excessus qui infinitus et omnem comparationem superans dici possit."
43 Zabarella 1597, 327e–328d.

actually used in making up the demonstrations, but science would be impossible without these principles, because they come into play before a demonstration can be made according to the proper principle appropriate for each science.[44] Common principles are not in a strict sense parts of the demonstration, but they are common notions without which the demonstration would be impossible. According to Zabarella Aristotle did not deny the use of these common principles in demonstration, but only their exclusive use.[45]

The principles of metaphysics are primary *simpliciter*; they have no other causes that are prior to them. The principles of other sciences are necessary only in proportion to the nature of their science, not absolutely necessary. Because metaphysics is the most valuable of all sciences, some writers think that all other speculative sciences are subalternated to it and that, as a result from this subalternation, their principles are derived from it. However, Zabarella denies this conclusion. He admits that the knowledge of the first principles used in metaphysics is obvious to man, and that they are more exact than the demonstrative principles of any science, which are always reducable to these first principles.[46]

There is, however, no direct use of these first principles of metaphysics in forming demonstrations in other sciences. Zabarella presents clear criteria for subalternation of different sciences. According to him, only in mathematics subalternation can be talked about, even if some have claimed that all the sciences are subalternated to metaphysics, or that the art of medicine is subalternated to the philosophy of nature. The both sciences in the subalternative relationship must have the same subject matter (*subiectum*), but the major science must be separated from the matter, whereas the other one must be connected to it. In arithmetic numbers are treated in an abstract way while in music, which is subalternated to mathematics, voice adds a perceptible quality to numbers. In the same way geometry deals with line separated from the senses, while the theory of perspective or optics

---

44  Zabarella 1597, 504f–505a.
45  Zabarella 1597, 774f–775a.
46  Zabarella 1597, 780c–f, 1267a–b.

combines line with sense of sight. This difference clarifies why, according to Zabarella it is possible to speak about subalternation only in mathematical sciences. Only mathematical things are in perceptive matter, but separated from it by contemplation.[47]

In Zabarella's view, the subalternative sciences must share the same subject matter and the same mode of consideration (*modus considerandi*). The subject matter of a science is the basis on which all that is considered in this science depends.[48] This is why Zabarella denies that the other sciences are directly dependent on metaphysics. The subject matter of metaphysics is being (*ens*) as being, but the subject matter of natural philosophy is being as having an inner principle of movement. Zabarella says that this difference may remind us of the difference between arithmetic and music, though according to him this comparison is not valid because natural philosophy adds the principle of movement to existence, which changes the whole way of consideration. The addition of music to arithmetic does not change the subject matter or the way of considering this science. Natural philosophy and metaphysics are thus two different sciences which cannot be compared with arithmetic and music.[49]

Metaphysics is an oddity among the sciences. The genus of the subject matter of a superior science is not usually the same as in subordinate sciences, but the subject matter of metaphysics is the genus of the subject matter of all other sciences. Metaphysics can prove all the principles of other sciences. It does so, however, only in metaphysics, not in the realm of special sciences. For example the principles of natural science must be proved through the principles proper to that science.[50] In this respect metaphysics comes near dialectics. Both these disciplines are common to all sciences because both treat common principles in their general scope, and not connected to some special genus. As Aristotle says in the second chapter of the first book of the *Topics*, dialectics tries to prove the principles of all sciences, but it can not do this with demonstrations, only through probable arguments. In Zabarella's view it is metaphysics which demonstrates the proper principles

---

47  Zabarella 1597, 523a–d.
48  Zabarella 1597, 526b–c.
49  Zabarella 1597, 528b–d.
50  Zabarella 1597, 528f–530a.

of special sciences, but even it cannot demonstrate common principles, and especially not two contradictory principles.[51]

There is another major difference between metaphysics and dialectics in Zabarella's view. As distinct from metaphysics, dialectics does not have any proper subject matter, but is able to make probable arguments of all possible things. The same thing distinguishes dialectics from proper logic; that is the art of demonstration. Demonstration is always applied to some special subject matter and the result of demonstration is science. The end of dialectics is not science and it has no proper subject matter, because the dialectical argument is not made of proper, but only of common principles. In fact dialectics cannot be called a science, either in a doctrinal, or in an applied sense of the word.[52]


## 2.5. The perfection of the philosophy of nature


In order to understand Zabarella's concept of science, it is important to consider his definition of nature and his ideas regarding the perfection of the philosophy of nature. The first book of Zabarella's collected works on natural sciences, *De rebus naturalibus libri XXX*, deals with the nature, order and perfection of natural philosophy. At the beginning of this work, called *De naturalis scientiae constitutione*, he emphasizes the fundamental importance of Aristotle's work in gaining knowledge of natural things. Many writers may have dealt with these matters, but nobody's books can be compared with Aristotle's.

Zabarella says that he himself begins his treatment of natural matters with a consideration of the nature of natural philosophy, just as Aristotle began his discussions of logic on consideration of the nature logic.[53] Zabarella emphasizes strongly the common character of the whole philosophy of nature. Because natural science is a unified science composed of one subject matter, all

51  Zabarella 1597, 809f–810d.
52  Zabarella 1597, 812c–e.
53  Zabarella, *De naturalis scientiae constitutione* 1590, 1b–2a.

natural beings must belong under the same genus, which is called the subject matter of the whole philosophy of nature. Natural beings have the principle of movement (*principium motus*) in themselves, which distinguishes them both from artistic matter and from mathematics, which belongs to the contemplative sciences.[54]

Following closely Aristotle's description in the *Physics* of what is natural (*naturale*), Zabarella states that it can be understood in three different ways. Firstly, through essence, when something is said to be natural for natural beings. Secondly the term natural means all the things considered in natural philosophy, like first matter which is called the natural principle (*principium naturale*), and movement which is called natural accident (*accidens naturale*) or natural thing (*res naturale*). Thirdly, and more narrowly, the term natural means all those who have a nature of some sort, that is a principle of movement as an inner property. Corporal things are the only things of this kind, since matter or movement are not natural. According to Zabarella, natural beings or essences defined only in this third sense are natural in a proper way. Errors can be avoided if we apply the term "natural" in this way only to those things which have an inner principle of movement.[55] Thus Zabarella achieves a definition of natural philosophy.

> The philosophy of nature is a contemplative science which presents a complete knowledge of those natural beings which have an inner principle of movement.[56]

The complete knowledge consists of knowledge both of principles and accidents, because the proper function of the philosophy of nature is to know the principles of natural beings, and their accidents through their causes. The whole science divides into two parts. The first part of natural science, which deals with the

---

54 Zabarella 1590, 3e,4c–d.
55 Zabarella 1590, 7g–8d.
56 Zabarella 1590, 15c: "Dicimus igitur Philosophiam naturalem esse scientiam contemplativam, quae naturalium corporum, quatenus principium motus in se habent, perfectam cognitionem tradit." This definition comes from Aristotle's *Physics* 193a28–29.

principles of natural beings, is included in the eight books of the *Physics*. The later part, which proceeds from the principles, is contained in the rest of the books of natural philosophy, the first of which is *De caelo* (On the heaven).[57] The same division can also be made on different grounds. According to the order of presentation, genus comes before species. So, in the philosophy of nature, the first universal part dealing with genus is included in the eight books of the *Physics*. The other, particular part, which contains the treatment of singular species, is incorporated into the rest of the books of natural philosophy. In Zabarella's view Aristotle's *Physics* deals with all that is common and universal for natural beings.[58]

Natural beings can also be understood in three ways. Firstly, they can be considered on the ground of their genus, without any reference to their species; secondly, as a collection of all species without any reference to genus; and, thirdly, by combining these two approaches, that is by a consideration of both genus and species. The first group is treated in the books of the *Physics*; the second group is explored in Aristotle's other works of natural philosophy, and the third group is considered in the whole science. To achieve a perfect philosophy of nature it is necessary to treat natural beings in all these ways, because the mere knowledge of the genus without the species would be incomplete; as would the opposite.[59]

> I ask, what is natural science if not a distinct and complete knowledge of natural beings through their causes? A scientific knowledge cannot be called confused or imperfect.[60]

Zabarella treats the question of the perfection of the natural sciences in a more detailed way in *De naturalis scientiae constitutione*. He claims that the book on minerals is necessary because the natural sciences are incomplete without it. It is

---

57 Zabarella 1590, 15c–f.
58 Zabarella 1590, 16f–17a.
59 Zabarella 1590, 17f–18b.
60 Zabarella 1597, 188e: "Quid enim, quaeso, est scientia naturalis, nisi perfecta et distincta rerum naturalium per suas causas cognitio? Confusa namque et imperfecta cognitio scientia dici non potest."

another question, however, whether Aristotle himself wrote about them.[61] In *De methodis* Zabarella states that Aristotle wrote about those things he wanted to write, but it is an exaggeration to claim that he would not have made any mistakes. Aristotle was no God in Zabarella's view, and it is false to insist that he knew the truth of everything he wrote. He was a remarkable man, nevertheless, and the first one who invented the logic and made a discipline out of it.[62] Zabarella did not, however, consider Aristotle's works as a complete *corpus*, where nothing could be added. In fact, it is a moot point, whether Aristotle himself wrote about minerals, but Zabarella knew well that in later times both Theophrastus and Albertus Magnus have written about this important subject. The place of the book on minerals in Aristotelian works on natural sciences is directly after the book *On meteorology*. Even if Aristotle himself did not write the book on minerals, he at least knew the importance of writing it in Zabarella's view.[63]

A treatise of special interest is the last chapter of *De naturalis scientiae constitutione*, where Zabarella discusses the question of perfection and the order of the natural sciences (*De perfectione Scientiae Naturalis ac de eius ordine*). Aristotle's philosophy of nature can be considered perfect in respect of its structure and form, but incomplete in terms of its reference to natural beings. There are many things that Aristotle did not treat and many things he did not even know. Though Aristotle did not deal with many plants and animals, it is still easy to point to there proper places in the Aristotelian system, and in his books on nature. Similarly, as regards mineralogy, it is easy to say that Aristotle himself did not write anything about minerals, yet his system allows us to place Albertus Magnus' book on minerals straight after the book on meteors.[64]

> We can say that Aristotle's philosophy of nature is complete and in every respect absolute in regard to subject matter and to things being considered; if not in practice, at least in theory. It can be seen that Aristotle did not only omit many things he did

---

61  Zabarella 1590, 76d–e.
62  Zabarella 1597, 331b.
63  Zabarella 1590, 77a, 80d–e.
64  Zabarella 1590, 119a–d.

not know, but he also left out many things he knew, but about which he did not want to write. Certainly there is no book or tractate written by Aristotle on the laughter of human beings or on the neighing of horses or other similar things; however, he planted the seed and made the basis from which even the things he did not write about can be known. In contemplating these things, we get much help from that which Aristotle taught us, and we can deduce knowledge from it.[65]

Zabarella compares Aristotle's natural science to the geometry and arithmetic of Euclid. There are many theorems which can be demonstrated from Euclid's works even if he did not actually write them. In Zabarella's view, there is no ground to judge his geometry or arithmetic defective or incomplete. If Euclid had wanted he could have demonstrated all these particular cases, but the book would have become so enormous that it surely would have daunted the reader.[66] According to Zabarella, this is why Euclid called his book *The Elements*, from which foundation all the other theorems can be demonstrated. In the same way Zabarella thinks that Aristotle's natural philosophy can be called perfect, since it deals with all the knowledge that it is possible for human intellect to attain, either in practice or in theory.[67]

---

65 Zabarella 1590, 119d–e: "Sed dicere preaterea possumus, naturalem philosophiam ab Aristotele scriptam etiam ratione materiae ac rerum cognoscendarum perfectam et omnibus numeris absolutam esse, si non actu, saltem virtute. Quandoquidem credendum omnino est, non solum praetermissa ab Aristotele fuisse multa, quoniam ipse fuerunt incognita, sed omissa etiam ab ipso plura fuisse, quae novit, sed scribere noluit. Nam certum est, nullum ab Aristotele scriptum fuisse librum, vel tractatum de hominis risibilitate, aut de hinnibilitate equi, aut de aliis similibus; tamen fundamenta ac semina quaedam ab eo iacta esse, unde emanare etiam illorum, quae non scripsit, cognitio potest. Iis enim, quae nos Aristoteles docuit, adiuti possumus alia multa contemplari et in eorum notitiam duci."
66 Zabarella 1590, 119f–120a: "Quamobrem id mihi de naturalibus Aristotelis libris dicendum videtur, quod ego dicere solitus sum de Geometricis et Arithmeticis ab Euclide scriptis. Etenim multa sunt Geometrica et Arithmetica theoremata, quae ab Euclide demonstrata non sunt; demonstrantur tamen ab aliis in ipsa librorum Euclidis interpretatione; nec ob id mancam et imperfectam vocare debemus Euclidis Geometriam vel Arithmeticam. Nam si omnia, quae de magnitudinibus ac de numeris demonstrari possunt, demonstrari Euclides voluisset, crevisset absque dubio volumen in immensum, quod quidem lectorem facile avertere ab illius lectione potuisset."
67 Zabarella 1590, 120a–120c.

# 3. Logic as an instrument of science

## 3.1. The nature of logic

E.J. Ashworth has recently noted the fact that nominalist logic very soon lost its prominent place in the Italian universities in the 1530's and 1540's.[1] The reasons for this are still somewhat obscure, but the result of this change in attitudes was that during the sixteenth century the principal questions about the nature of logic again came under consideration. Among Paduan Aristotelians, too, a vivid discussion about the nature of logic arose.

At the beginning of the sixteenth century there was at the University of Padua a strong scholastic, or rather scotist, tendency to define logic as a science.[2] Zabarella rejects this definition, by denying that logic is a science, art or even a faculty. Instead he returns to Aristotle's ancient Greek commentators who stressed

---

1  Ashworth 1982, 1988a, 1988b. The sixteenth-century Aristotelian logic has not yet been studied very thoroughly. Risse 1964 offers vast material, but not always in a very systematic form. Ashworth 1974 makes some basic distinctions when she discusses the questions concerning the nature of logic (pp.26–37), but her material is not very large because the nature of logic is not the main topic of her study.

2  Both Thomas Aquinas and Duns Scotus had defined logic as a science. Thomas Aquinas, *In I Post. Anal.* 1,n.1: "Et haec ars est logica, idest rationalis scientia." Duns Scotus, *Quaestiones super universalia Porphyrii*, in *Opera omnia* (reprint Hildesheim 1968),q.I,fol.87,2: "Dicendum quod logica est scientia, quae enim in ea docentur, demonstrative concluduntur sicut in aliis scientiis; ergo sciuntur ... Intelligendum est tamen, quod logica dupliciter consideratur. Unomodo in quantum est docens et sic ex necessariis et propriis

the instrumental value of logic. Alexander of Aphrodisias,[3] Ammonius[4] and Philoponus[5] all pointed out that logic is more an instrument of science than a science itself. Zabarella was not the first Paduan writer who turned his eye to these Greek commentators, however. As a result of humanist text critique, the scholastic writers and Averroes' texts were increasingly compared with the classical sources.

Within these sixteenth-century discussions at Padua on the nature of logic, two central topics can be identified: the subject matter and the use (or the end) of logic. A definition of the whole discipline of logic can be formed from these two. In Zabarella's opinion, the nature of every discipline depends on the subjects under consideration. From those things which logic concerns itself with, we notice immediately, that it cannot be a science.

In order to demonstrate this claim, he makes a division between first and second notions.[6] Whereas a philosopher deals with first notions (*primae notiones*), a logician deals with second notions (*secundae notiones or secundo intellecta*). First notions, like an

---

principiis procedit ad necessarias conclusiones et sic est scientia. Alio modo in quantum utimur ea applicando eam ad illa in quibus est usus et sic non est ex propriis, sed ex communibus, nec sic est scientia." See Bottin 1973, 45; Bottin 1979, 284; Edwards 1960, 100 and Schmidt 1966, 3–15. On scotist influence at the University of Padua in general, see the articles in *La tradizione scotista Veneto-Padovana* 1979.

3 Alexandri Aphrodisiensis, *In octo Topicorum Aristotelis libros explanatio* 1573, 39B,40B: " ... vel logicae sunt, quas ipse tum significavit, cum diceret, eas afferre adiumentum ad aliquid aliud eius generis, ostendens logicam instrumentum esse et adhiberi, tanquam adiumentum aliquod ad aliud afferrat ... Logicae autem sunt hae, quae sunt ad aliquid, simul sunt natura; eandem in contrariis scientiam versari; repugnantiam verum et falsum distinguere."

4 Ammonius Hermeae F, *In Porphyrii Institutionem Aristotelis Categorias et librum De interpretatione* 1569, 12: " ... sub logicen, quae philosophiae instrumentum appellatur, hic liber reducitur ... Logice non est philosophiae pars illa quidem, sed instrumentum."

5 Ioannes Grammatici Alexandrei cognomento Philoponi, *In libros Priorum resolutivorum Aristotelis commentarie annotationes* 1553, f.3r: " ... Similiter itaque philosophia logicem tanquam instrumentum sibi suum adaptat ..." For these Greek commentators view on the nature of logic, see Edwards 1960, 149–152; Antonaci 1971, 138–142.

6 This distinction between first and second intentions or impositions was common in medieval logic. On the history of this distinction see Knudsen 1982 and Schmidt 1966, 94–129.

animal or a human being, refer directly to things through mental concepts. The first notions which refer to things outside the mind, like heaven, elements or stars, are not created by human beings. Even if man names them, they exist regardless of him.

Second notions (like genus, species, noun, verb, proposition) relate directly to first notions, and thus only indirectly to things. Second notions are created by the human mind. The term "human being" or "horse", is a genus or a noun defining a second notion. So the existence of second notions is dependent upon our knowledge, and they rather define first notions than things.[7] According to Zabarella logic is concerned entirely with second notions made by human beings, and which therefore exist or do not exist according to our will. These are not necessary but contingent, and therefore cannot be termed a proper science, because science deals only with necessary things.[8]

This definition of second notions as the subject-matter of logic leads Zabarella straight to the second topic, namely the definition of logic as a science, an art or something else. Even if it is obvious that logic cannot be called a proper science because its subject-matter is only contingent, it can be called a science when logic is applied to scientific things. Zabarella asks, what else is natural philosophy than logic being applied into natural things? When it is applied to scientific material, however, logic is called natural philosophy, arithmetic or something other than logic. This is based on the distinction between proper logic (*logica docens*) and applied logic (*logica utens*). The basic meaning of the word logic is to teach and contemplate scientific methods, which is not science. Besides this meaning it is possible to speak about applied logic,

---

7  Zabarella 1597, 6a–c. Zabarella makes the same division when discussing the nature of the sense of sight in his books on natural philosophy. Zabarella, *De visu*, first book, in *De rebus naturalibus* 1590, 789f–790a.

8  Zabarella 1597, 7e. Some earlier Paduan writers had the same opinion about the subject matter of logic. For example Girolamo Balduino wrote in his *Expositio* 1563, f.202r: "Vera ac peripathetica opinio de subiecto totali et adaequato logices ex Arist. et Aver. excerpta est, quae secundo intellecta ut instrumenta notificandi sunt subiectum totale et adaequatum in logica." Also Alessandro Piccolomini defined the second intentions as the proper material for the logician to deal with. Piccolomini A, *L'instrumento de la filosofia* 1556, 33.

but as a matter of fact it is not logic anymore, but natural philosophy or mathematics.[9]

Zabarella appears to be considering logic as nearer the arts than the sciences. Logic and the arts do share a common subject matter. Arts and logic also have a common scope and end, both of which differentiate them from sciences.[10] In the proper meaning of the word, however, logic cannot be called an art. In the second book of *Physics* Aristotle separates art from nature. According to Zabarella nature operates in itself, but in art the origin is in the maker and not in the thing made.[11] This operation is only possible within natural things, however. So every work of art is corporal, and its creation material, involving the instrumental help of hands and legs and other parts of our bodies. In this the arts differ from logic, which is a habit of mind. Logic takes place in the mind, and has no bodily connection; it is mind's work without matter.[12]

Zabarella is not even satisfied with the the claim that logic is a faculty (*facultas*). If a faculty is so defined that it includes all theoretical, active and productive disciplines, then we can call logic a faculty. If, however, we follow Alexander of Aphrodisias, in his preface to *Topics*, and define a faculty as a power which considers two contradictory claims, we cannot accept logic as a faculty. Although Aristotle defines dialectics as a faculty in his first book of *Rhetorics*, he does not take dialectics to mean the whole discipline of logic, but only the disputary part of it. Thus, according to Zabarella, when Aristotle says that dialectics is a faculty he is referring not to whole logic, but only to one special part of it. The discipline as a whole cannot be called a faculty.[13]

---

9  Zabarella 1597, 10d–11f. Duns Scotus and other medieval writers had already made the division between *logica docens* and *utens*. According to Scotus, however, it is the *docens* part of logic that is science, not the applied logic.
10  Zabarella 1597, 8c.
11  Zabarella 1597, 16f: "Ideo Aristoteles in 2.lib.Physic. dicit artem esse principium operandi in alio. Hoc enim discrimine artem separat a natura, quae natura est principium operationis in receptae in eo ipso, in quo natura inest, quam nostri immanentem operationem vocant. Ars vero est principium operationis in alio, quam transeuntem appellant. Propterea in ipso artis opere ars non inest, sed extra est, nempe in animo artificis." See chapter 5.2. for a more detailed discussion on art and nature in Zabarella's philosophy.
12  Zabarella 1597, 17a–c.
13  Zabarella 1597, 18c–20e.

Having rejected all definitions he considers incorrect, Zabarella finally gives his own. The Greek commentators on Aristotle had defined logic as an instrument of science; a definition which, according to Zabarella, cannot be bettered. The genus of logic is an instrumental discipline or an instrumental habit.[14] In Zabarella's view, there are two instrumental disciplines: grammar and logic. Both are instruments of philosophy but in different ways. Grammar is necessary and precedes all other disciplines, because it teaches writing according to rules. Logic proceeds from grammar by considering the meanings of words.[15] Logic is an intellectual instrumental habit which helps the mind to adopt the other habits. However, Zabarella does not think that logic belongs to the same group with the other five habits mentioned in the *Nicomachean Ethics*, because the dignity and utility of logic are not internal, but are defined by external ends.[16]

According to Zabarella, logic can also be subdivided into its natural and artificial elements. Natural logic (*logica naturalis*) contains those means of reasoning and argument which human beings have by birth, and which lack formal rules. By artificial logic (*logica artificiosa*) he means those formal syllogistic rules which Aristotle first developed for the use of philosophy. In Zabarella's view, inference would only be possible in natural logic

---

14 Zabarella 1597, 21a. In the Middle Ages the definition of logic as a science went often hand in hand with emphasis of the instrumental value of it. For example, Thomas Aquinas, *Expositio super librum Boethii De trinitate*, 5, 1 ad 2: "Res autem quibus est logica non quaeruntur ad cognoscendum propter seipsas, sed ut adminiculum quoddam ad alias scientias. Et ideo logica non continentur sub speculativa philosophia quasi principalis pars, sed sicut quoddam reductum ad philosophiam speculativam, prout ministrat speculationi sua instrumenta, scilicet syllogismos et definitiones et alia huiusmodi; quibus in speculativis scientiis indigemus. Unde ... non tam est scientia quam scientiae instrumentum." See Schmidt 1966, 24–31. Also William Ockham laid emphasis on the instrumental nature of logic. Ockham, *Summa logicae*, Epist.proem, 9–12: "Logica enim est omnium artium aptissimum instrumentum, sine qua nulla scientia perfecte sciri potest, quae non more materialium instrumentorum usu crebro consumitur, sed per cuiuslibet alterius scientiae studiosum exercitium continuum recipit incrementum."
15 Zabarella 1597, 23b–d.
16 Zabarella 1597, 24c–f.

with great effort and difficulty. That is why Aristotle invented artificial logic to make our reasoning easier.[17]

## 3.2. The use of logic

In Zabarella's view all the instruments used by logic can be reduced to syllogisms. For him the making of syllogisms is the universal end of logic, and their demonstration its particular end.[18] The subject matter of logic is all possible things as they are in second notions. Thus Zabarella defines logic as an intellectual instrumental habit, which makes second notions from the concepts of things. By the instrument of logic the truth can be separated from falsity.[19]

Zabarella, however, was not the first Paduan writer since the Greek commentators to define logic as an instrument of all sciences. Earlier in the century Marcantonio Zimara and Girolamo Balduino had already abandoned the scholastic definition and discussed in a fresh way the proper nature of logical disciplines. In a manuscript, which he had probably written during his first Paduan period (1500–1509), Zimara discusses the nature of logic and other disciplines.[20] He disagreed with the scotist writers who wanted to define logic as a science, and refers to Alexander of Aphrodisias' commentary on Aristotle's *Topics*, where he claims

---

17 Zabarella 1597, 27b–c. Bernardino Tomitano, Zabarella's teacher in logic, had already dealt with this distinction, which, in addition, is a common part of scholastic tradition. Tomitano had made a stronger claim, however, by claiming that artificial logic is not only useful but necessary to human beings. Without it we cannot know the truth, but are for the most part doomed to make fallacies in our reasoning. See Simionato 1973, 117.

18 Zabarella 1597, 42f,44f–45a.

19 Zabarella 1597, 52c: "Est enim logica habitus intellectualis instrumentalis, seu disciplina instrumentalis a Philosophis ex Philosophiae habitu genita, quae secundas notiones in conceptibus rerum fingit et fabricat, ut sint instrumenta, quibus in omni re verum cognoscatur et a falso discernatur."

20 MS VIII G.97, Biblioteca Nazionale di Napoli. I have used Antonaci's references and citations of the manuscript. Marcantonio Zimara (1475–1532) taught logic and natural philosophy at the University of Padua in the beginning of the sixteenth century and again in the 1520's. On his life and works see CHRP 1988, 841; Lohr 1982, 245–254 and Antonaci 1971,1978.

logic to be an instrument of science. In this manuscript Zimara ends up with a definition of logic as a mode of science which, in theoretical disciplines, discerns truth from false, and in practical disciplines, good from bad.[21] Almost the same definition is given in Zimara's later printed works, *Tabula* and *Theoremata*. In *Theoremata* Zimara, however, mentions the double use of logic for the theoretical and the practical disciplines, but considers the first one as a primary use.[22]

Girolamo Balduino, however, interpreted Zimara as claiming logic as a science. According to Balduino, he did not quite understand the instrumental character of this discipline.[23] For Balduino himself, logic was neither a science, nor an art, nor an instrument, but a faculty (*facultas organorum*) which serves all arts and sciences.[24] As Edwards has noted, this definition is not far from the definition of logic as an instrument.[25] Many of Balduino's pupils followed his definition and when their teacher himself was not very eager to publish his lectures, they mediated his thoughts. For example Angelo Tio (Thyus) wrote that logic is not a science or an art, but an instrumental discipline.[26] Alessandro Piccolomini takes the same position when he says that logic is not a science, but

---

21  Antonaci 1971, 139.
22  Zimara 1556, prop.58: "Logica usitatur in scientiis duobus modis, aut secundum quod est instrumentum distinguens verum a falso et hic est modus proprius; aut secundum quod declarata in ea accipiuntur pro maximis in destruendo, aut construendo aliquid, et ista consideratio cum usitatur in artibus particularibus est non propria: in arte autem universali, idest in prima Philosophia est propria." Zimara gives the same definition, almost verbatim, also in prop.49. As a matter of fact, this definition is copied from Averroes' commentary on the *Physics*, book I, comm.35. See also Antonaci 1971, 148–149.
23  Papuli 1967, 48–49. On the life and works of Girolamo Balduino see Lohr 1974, 257; Papuli 1967, 57–78 and Edwards 1960, 102–103. Only few facts about Balduino's life and activities are known.
24  Balduino, *Quaesitum primum, An logica sit scientia vel ars*. In Balduino 1563, 195–199. Ibid 198b: "Quod logica neque scientia, neque ars, neque vere instrumentum est, sed vere et appropriate dicitur et est facultas organorum seu rerum, quarum finis est, ut sint instrumenta deservientia omnibus artibus et scientiis."
25  Edwards 1960, 109.
26  Angelo Thyus, *De subiecto logicae* in 1547, fol.19v: "Cognito, quae facultas sit ipsa logica, scilicet quod nec ars, nec scientia, sed tertium genus, scilicet instrumentaria ad cognoscendum alias artes et scientias." Angelo Tio died in 1559 and was professor of logic at Padua in the late 1540's, see Edwards 1960, 101 and Lohr 1982, 194.

an instrument, the purpose of which is to distinguish true from false in the theoretical sciences and good from bad in the practical ones.[27]

Zabarella's professor of logic, Bernardino Tomitano, however, tried to reconcile the "Latin" view of logic as a science with the "Greek" view of it as an instrument. Human life has two aspects according to Tomitano: a theoretical one, of which the truth is the end and a practical one, where we aim at the good.[28] Logic is an instrument for human beings to discern true from false and good from bad.[29] When science is defined in a common way as a certain knowledge of truth, however, logic can also be called a science, since the object of logic is truth.[30]

In these definitions of logic, however, two different things ought to be clarified. In the definition of logic modern scholars have mainly paid attention to whether it is a science, an art or an

---

27 Alessandro Piccolomini, *L'instrumento de la filosofia* 1551, 21,33: "Hor' aplicando tutte queste cose, á proposito de la dubitation mossa di sopra, dico che col discorso naturale et con la logica data ad ogni huomo da la natura, fu dà prima per aiuto de la Filosofia, trovata una logica artificiosa, per la quale fur fabricati con arte et con regole, i sillogismi che dovevano essere instrumento à l'acquisto de la notitia del vero et del buono ... Dico tornando a proposito che per questa cagione la Logica non scientia reale, ò parte de la Filosofia si destimare, m·a· solo instrumento di quella." See also Edwards 1960, 109–110. On the life and works of Alessandro Piccolomini (1508–1579), see CHRP 1988, 831; Lohr 1980, 624–625, and Cerreta 1960.

28 Bernardino Tomitano (1517–1576) did not publish very many books and most of his known works have survived only in manuscripts. *Lectiones XVI logicae*, in Biblioteca Marciana Venice cod.lat. VI 295/2889), f.4r–v: "Vita humana duplici vita utitur, speculativa et activa ... speculativae partis obiectum est veritas, activae bonum ... cum veritati iungatur falsitas, cum bono malum." I have not been able to see this manuscript myself, but have relied on Giustina Simionato's description of it, see Simionato 1973, 116. The same opinion about the use of logic for the both parts of philosophy, speculative and active, is introduced in Tomitano's *Contradictionum solutiones* 1562, f.37r, where Tomitano relies on Averroes and says that logic can be applied to all kind of things.

29 Tomitano, *Lectiones super primo libro Posteriorum Aristotelis* 1558, (MS. 810 in Biblioteca Universitaria at Padua), 5r: "Ioannes Scotus tenet, quod logica possit vocari scientia speculativa, nos autem tenemus cum optimis peripateticis, quod ipsa non sit nisi instrumentum, aut instrumentaria facultas, ... quo instrumento utitur philosophus ad distinctionem veri a falso, et boni a malo." I have used Edwards' paraphrase and citations of Tomitano's manuscript, see Edwards 1960, 114.

30 Ibid, 5r: "Quomodo ergo vocatur scientia, si est instrumentum tantum? Dico quod vocatur scientia communiter accepta. Nam hoc nomen, scientia, est

instrument of science. As far as this classification is concerned, Zabarella agrees with most of the Paduan writers that logic is an instrument of science, not a science itself. But this distinction between the "Latin" and the "Greek" view of logic is far too simple to clarify Zabarella's position in this matter entirely. Besides this distinction, he makes another qualification in the definition of logic, which is as important as the first one for our present subject, and in which Zabarella disagrees with most of these former Paduan writers; namely the use or the end of logic.

As we have seen, the principal definition of logic as an instrument of all arts and sciences was a common feature of these sixteenth century writers on logic, at least in Venetian Aristotelianism. This definition resembles Zabarella's use of the word, but there seems to be one interesting difference, because he emphasized the role of logic primarily in the speculative sciences. In *De natura logicae* Zabarella dedicates a whole chapter called *De fine logicae* (Of the end of logic) to this problem, where he argues against the definition of logic as an instrument both for the speculative sciences and the practical disciplines.

In this chapter Zabarella first comments on the prevailing definition of logic as an instrument which separates truth from false and good from bad. According to him many writers try to convince their readers with the passage of the first book of the *Topics*, where Aristotle had claimed logic to be useful both for theoretical sciences and for practical disciplines. In Zabarella's opinion, no proof can be found for their case in the words of Aristotle, for he does not mention the separation of good from bad in this connection. Thus this addition is unnecessary and, what is even worse, it makes the definition of logic incorrect.[31] According to Zabarella, even Averroes understood this when he defined logic

valde latum, interdum enim scientia definitur, quod sit veri certa cognitio ... hoc modo dicimus logicam esse scientiam, quia obiectum logicae est veritas." See Edwards 1960, 114.

31 Zabarella 1597, 30b: "Mihi tamen haec sententia non probatur. Puto enim satis esse, si dicamus finem logicae esse discernere in philosophia verum a falso, quasi dicamus cognitionem esse totius logicae finem. De bono autem et malo nullam faciendam esse mentionem, sed supervacaneam esse hanc additionem et in definitione vitiosam, quod quidem facile ostendemus." See also ibid. 32d–33a. Zabarella is right on this point, because Aristotle does not discuss the question of the usefulness of logic for practical disciplines in this passage of *Topics* (105b19–29).

as an instrument of science which discerns truth from false but said nothing of good or bad.[32]

Zabarella says that every art has a theoretical or informative, and an operative part. Logic belongs above all to the earlier, which forms knowledge for the latter to apply. A builder can use logic in the art of building but not in the actual building process, because logic aims at knowledge, not operation.[33] Thus logic is primarily connected to contemplative sciences and only secondarily to active and operative disciplines. Both practical and productive disciplines regard logic as useful, but it is not as useful for them as for the contemplative sciences.[34]

Zabarella's chapter on the definition of logic follows his general philosophical attitude which stresses the importance of theoretical sciences, as against practical or productive ones. The division between natural and artificial things is essential for him, for he defines logic above all as a mental instrument, not a material one,

---

32 Zabarella 1597, 32d: "Hoc videtur Averroes non ignorasse, qui in Commentario 35.primi libri Physicorum et in Epitome Metaphysicae tractatu secundo, capite primo, dicit logicam esse instrumentum, quo discernitur verum a falso; nihil dicit de bono et malo." Zabarella is right here, too. Averroes, *Epitome in librum Metaphysicae Aristotelis*, in *Aristotelis Opera cum Averrois commentariis*, vol. VIII, f.172v: "Quia res, quae declarantur in arte logicali, exercentur ut diximus alibi dupliciter, vel scilicet ex eo quae sunt instrumenta et methodi et regulae dirigentes intellectum et custodientes ipsum ab errore et hoc est proprium artificium illorum." In the mentioned passage of Averroes'commentary on the *Physics*, he refers, however, both to theoretical and practical sciences, but speaks nothing about good or bad.

33 Zabarella 1597, 31c: "Quum enim et artis cuiusque et moralis disciplinae duae sint partes: una docens et cognitionem tradens, altera operans; logica est instrumentum, quo pars docens utitur. Nam aedificator potest quidem arte logica uti in tradenda arte aedificatoria, sed non in operatione et domus constructione; logica itaque secundum propriam naturam cognitionem ut finem respicit, non operationem. Cognitio vero est veri et falsi per se, non est boni ac mali, nisi ex accidenti."

34 Zabarella 1597, 33b–d: "Ex his, quae modo diximus, sumitur ratio cur logica sit praecipue instrumentum philosophiae contemplativae, aliarum autem disciplinarum secundario. Nam logica est instrumentum per se conferens ad cognoscendum, non per se ad operandum. Disciplinae igitur ut cognitione, ita et logicae utilitate participant. Contemplativae quidem per se et primario cognitionem quaerunt et praeterea nihil, ideo ad eas primario logica confert. Activae autem et artes omnae cognitionem non praecipue, sed secundario quaerunt; propterea logica secundario harum instrumentum est. Quod autem appellari soleat instrumentum philosophiae tum contemplativae, tum activae, nec ita dicatur artium instrumentum, id non fit quia magis ad activam philosophiam, quam ad artes conferat, siquidem ad has omnes aequalis est

such as are useful for arts. In other words, apart from the theoretical sciences, the utility of logic is limited to the theoretical part of every *tekhne*. In the actual operating or manufacturing process there is no use of logic.

Girolamo Balduino saw logic as a major instrument not only for theoretical sciences, but also for practical disciplines and productive arts and, above all, for medicine, which he considered the noblest of all arts.[35] In company with Zabarella, Balduino restricts the use of logic in practical and productive disciplines to their cognitive rather than their operative aspects. Yet every art and practical discipline requires reason and Balduino saw logic as necessary also for these disciplines. In this, Balduino differs from Zabarella. For example, surgery has both a cognitive and an operative part; logic being necessary for the cognitive part, which precedes the operative one.[36]

---

logicae utilitas et minor, quam ad contemplativas. Sed ratio eius sumitur ex consilio et scopo generantis; philosophi namque logicam genuerunt et propter philosophiam, non propter artes, idcirco philosophiae, non artium instrumentum dicitur." Edwards notes this distinction, too, but fails to see this as a break with former Paduan tradition, because he ignores the importance of the division between theoretical and practical subjects and disciplines in Zabarella's philosophy. See Edwards 1960, 147–148.

35  Balduino, *Variis generis in logica quaesita* 1569, f.25: "Probavimus clare et vere logicam, ratione artium, praecipue dirigi ad medicinam, cum inter illa artes magis usitata, magis necessaria et magis oscura et ignota ... medicina inter artes magis necessaria, quia tractat de vita, ultra quia est naturaliter nobis insita: aliae artes vel non sunt de vita, ut civilis, vel non naturaliter insitae, ut legalis; ... magis medicina usitatur, non autem sic sunt caeterae artes, ex quo potest teneri logicam dirigi principaliter ad medicinam loquendo secundum usum." Unfortunately I have not been able to locate this edition of Balduino's work and I have relied on Papuli's description and citations of it; see Papuli 1967, 200.

36  Ibid, f.22–23: "Artes activae et factivae acquiruntur ex praecedenti cognitione: ergo quaelibet doctrina et disciplina factiva et activa utitur necessario logicalibus instrumentis ... Scire accipitur communiter pro notificare et sic non tantum usus logices est ad tres scientias, sed etiam ad omnes alias, ...principalis ad perfectiores et principaliores artes: ...metaphysica, matematica et naturalis; medicina, legalis incluendo moralem, ... nautica, astrologia, chirurgia, theologia et, ut universaliter dicam, omnes artes quae acquiruntur discursu intellectus ... Quaelibet ars perfecta activa et factiva habet duo: unum est cognitio rei agendae seu faciendae, aliud est factio et actio; ...artem et scientiam quamlibet dividi in duas partes, scilicet in cognitionem rerum quas docet et instrumenta et logicam qua ducit, facit concludit et invenit illam cognitionem ... Ad illas artes et scientias logica est

Indeed, Balduino's description of the usefulness of logic reminds us of Zabarella's; however Balduino did not stress the difference between different kind of disciplines. Nevertheless, Zabarella's definition of logic as an instrument mainly for the theoretical sciences brought about an immediate response at the University of Padua. A few years later Bernardino Petrella wrote a book about the nature of logic, where he claims that logic not only aims at cognition, but sometimes at action. He does not explicitly name Zabarella, but he criticizes those writers who try to restrict logic as instrumental only in the theoretical sciences. These writers deny the usefulness of logic to practical disciplines by claiming that the aim of logic lies solely in cognition, which is found in all disciplines, and that defining good and bad within logic is unnecessary.[37]

Petrella notes that only in the contemplative sciences does cognition exist for its own sake. In all other disciplines it precedes operation. In moral disciplines, action is the end towards which all cognition is aimed. If we really want logic to be an instrument of both parts of philosophy, active and contemplative, criteria of good and bad must be added to the definition of logic.[38] So Petrella ends up by defining logic as an instrumental discipline which

---

necessaria, quae sunt rationales, ergo ad omnes; probatur quod nemo ad sensum enim facit, agit aliquid nisi ratione, cum motu et discursu intellectus ... Dubitabis, chirurgia fit manibus, ergo operativa et manualis ... Respondeo: chirurgia habet duo, quorum unum est cognitio, aliud est operatio per illam cognitionem. Dicatur quod primo modo non manualis est neque operativa, et sic ad ipsam logica est necessaria." See Papuli 1967, 196–197.

37  Petrella, *Logicarum disputationum libri septem* 1584, 6–7: "Hanc quam sequimur, opinionem quo ad externum Logicae finem, adaequatumque Logici operantis subiectum nonnulli mordicus nituntur impugnare et primum quo ad externum Logicae finem asserunt, eam de bono et malo additionem supervacaneam esse, quoniam ex eorum sententia totius Logicae finis est cognitio; quamobrem satis esse putant, ut dicatur, externum Logicae finem esse discernere in philosophia verum a falso, quia verum et falsum, eorumque cognitio non modo in contemplativa, sed etiam in Activa philosophia et in omnibus Artibus locum habent." On the life and works of Bernardino Petrella (1529–1595) see Lohr 1979, 577–579. Petrella taught logic at Padua at least in the 1560's.

38  Petrella 1584, 8: " ... quoniam si hac de causa philosophus in Moralibus finem, ac scopum activae philosophiae actionem nominare maluit, quam cognitionem; eo quia actio principalem locum tenet, cum sit ultimus, ac praecipuus finis, ad quem omnis earum disciplinarum cognitio dirigitur et per quem activa a contemplativa philosophia secernitur ... Ita etiam nos hoc

serves both theoretical and practical philosophy by distinguishing truth from false and good from bad.[39]

Like Tomitano, Petrella wanted to define logic both as an instrument of science and a science itself. According to Petrella, Duns Scotus had claimed proper logic (*logica docens*) was a science, but when logic is applied to things (*logica utens*), it is no longer science. Petrella himself draws the same conclusion, but uses the words real science and rational science in place of *scientia realis* and *scientia rationalis*. Logic is not a real science, but it is a rational science in an absolute way.[40] What is noteworthy in this distinction, is that Zabarella held the entirely opposite opinion. As we have seen, he felt that *logica docens* could never be a science, but logic applied to scientific material can be called a science, even if the titles natural philosophy, mathematics and so on should be preferred.

Many of Zabarella's followers at the University of Padua were satisfied with his definition of this discipline. Francesco Piccolomini defined logic in Zabarellian terms as an instrument of science which distinguished truth from falsity.[41] Cesare Cremonini

---

nomine addimus discernere bonum a malo, ut magis significare possimus mentem philosophi de Logica esse, ut instrumentum sit utriusque partis philosophiae. Quod fieri non potest per id solum, ut discernat verum a falso, quia licet verum et falsum, eorumque cognitio non tantum in contemplativa philosophia, sed etiam in activa locum habeant. Manifestius tamen per activa per id, ut discernat bonum a malo, quam per id, ut discernat verum a falso significatur. Sicuti ergo non poterat aliter loqui philosophus de fine et scopo activae philosophiae in Moralibus, ita nos aliter non possumus externum Logicae finem ponere, si ex mente philosophi exprimere volumus; Logicam utriusque partis philosophiae instrumentum esse."

39  Petrella 1584, 10: "Logica est disciplina instrumentaria probans instrumenta utrique philosophiae parti inservientia ad secernendum verum a falso, bonumque a malo."

40  Petrella 1584, 11: "Respondens ad hanc philosophi auctoritatem, ait, Aristotelem ibi distinguere scientias reales, ideo consequentiam non valere, quia licet Logica non sit scientia realis, est tamen scientia rationalis, quod sat est ade ostendendum, Logicam esse absolute scientiam. Ex qua responsione indicat dari scientiam communem ad realem et rationalem, nec non declarat de qua scientia intelligat, quando asserit, Logicam esse scientiam. Est itaque logica scientia rationalis docens construere modos seu instrumenta notificandi utrique philosophiae parti inservientia." On Petrella's relationship with the scotist tradition, see Bottin 1979, 283.

41  Piccolomini, *Discursus ad universam logicam attinens* 1603, discursus 2: "Definiri potest logica quod sit disciplina quae in secundis notionibus

used the same definition and the same reason that Zabarella had given, in order to restrict the usefulness of logic to the theoretical sciences only. Even practical sciences deal in language; and we can always consider the truth and fallacy of its statements.[42]

Zabarella's concept of logic became popular also in Germany. *Opera logica* was published at Basel in 1594, and by the turn of the seventeenth century most of German Aristotelians had learned their logic by means of Zabarella's texts. Among this group was Johannes Jungius (1587–1657), who had studied medicine at Padua in 1618. The impact of Zabarella's definition of logic as an instrumental discipline on the work of Jungius is evident. According to Jungius, logic is a mental art leading to the discernment of truth from falsity.[43] Zabarella's pupil at Padua, Giulio Pace (Julius Pacius, 1550–1635), who later moved to Germany, defined logic as a intellectual art. The end of logic in his view is the scientific discernment of truth from false.[44]

---

versatur, ut sunt instrumenta cognoscendi et prae™sertim sciendi ...ut ...verum a falso secernatur ..." This citation is taken from Risse 1964, 292. On Fransesco Piccolomini (1523–1607), see Baldini 1980a,; CHRP 1988, 831 and Lohr 1980, 626–639. Piccolomini was aprofessor of natural philosophy at Padua between 1560–1598.

42 Cremonini Cesare, *Logica sive Dialectica* 1663, 5: "Dubitatur etiam quando dicimus, quod est facultas videndi verum et falsum; dicet aliquis, ergo non serviet morali, qui versatur circa bonum et malum. Respondetur, quod bonum et malum circa quod versatur moralis, est bonum consultabile, unde ad tale bonum concurrit discursus, in quo discursu est veritas et falsitas." On the life and works of Cremonini (1550–1631), who in 1601 succeeded Francesco Piccolomini in the chair of natural philosophy at Padua, see Lohr 1975, 728–739. Cremonini held different chairs at the University of Padua between 1591 and 1631.

43 Jungius, *Logica Hamburgiensis* 1638, 1: "Logica est ars mentis nostrae operationes dirigens ad verum a falso discernendum." On Jungius see Lohr 1977, 737–738. More on Zabarella's impact on Jungius, see Rudolf W. Meyer's preface in Jungius 1957, XVI.

44 Pace, *Institutiones logicae* 1596, 1r. Cited from Risse 1964, 454: "Logica est ars ratiocinandi, ut discernatur verum a falso. Finis igitur logicae est scientia, qua dignoscitur verum a falso." On Pace (1550–1635) see Lohr 1979, 546–547; Vasoli 1974, 651–777 and Vasoli 1983. Similar definitions can be found in the logical writings of Jungius' and Pace's contemporaries. Fortunatus Crellius writes in his *Isagoge logica* 1584, 1, that logic is an organic habit which can discern truth from false. Cited from Risse 1964, 453: "Logica est habitus organicus, verum a falso discernere potis." On Crellius, see Lohr 1975, 727–728. According to Cornelius Martini (1570–1649), logic is an instrumental mental habit or an instrumental discipline, which teaches us to form second

# 3.3. Rhetoric and poetry as logical disciplines

Zabarella begins the second book of *De natura logicae* with a question about the two parts of logic and their respective order. At the beginning of his *Posterior Analytics*, Aristotle divides logic into universal and particular. According to this division, which was also followed by Zabarella, universal logic contains *Categories, De Interpretatione* and *Prior Analytics*. To particular logic is left *Posterior Analytics, Topics* and *Sophistical Refutations*.[45] A logician needs some kind of foreknowledge when he is forming second notions. That is why, Aristotle when he began to consider logic, placed first a book dealing with categories, which formed an introduction to the whole of universal logic. For Zabarella, Aristotle's *Categories* does not constitute an actual part of logic itself, but is an introduction to the whole discipline.[46]

According to Zabarella, particular logic is necessary because, in *Prior Analytics,* the handling of logic is harsh and far from actual use. The instruments of universal logic do not help us very much to know things, if they are not applied to some particular end. In Zabarella's view our mind is like an empty board (*tabula rasa*) when we are born. We cannot reach complete knowledge of things immediately, but only after hard work and contemplation. Moving from complete ignorance to full knowledge is impossible without some intermediary steps. Thus we must at first accept a harsh and incomplete knowledge, which is then followed by a complete one.[47]

Though complete knowledge is attained by demonstration, this is not the initial step in reasoning; first comes sophistry, then dialectics and only thirdly the art of demonstration. With

---

notions from first ones. These are instruments by which truth can be discerned from falsity. Martini, *Commentatiorum logicorum adversus Ramistas libri V* 1623, 39. Cited from Risse 1964, 456: "Logicam esse habitum mentis instrumentalem sive disciplinam instrumentalem, quae secundas notiones in rerum conceptibus primis fingere doceat, ut sint instrumenta, quibus in omni re verum a falso distinguatur." On Martini see Lohr 1978, 568–569.

45  Zabarella 1597, 53b.
46  Zabarella 1597, 62b–d.
47  Zabarella 1597, 70d–72b.

sophistry we solve the fallacies which prevent us from seeing the truth; and the art of dialectics teaches us to confirm any problem with a probable argument. In the third stage, we confirm our knowledge of these opinions (*opiniones*) by means of demonstration.

In *Posterior Analytics*, Aristotle teaches the use of demonstration, but according to Zabarella we cannot always use it. This is due either to our own incapacity to understand the causes or the qualities of the subjects of a science. In such cases dialectics can help us in two different ways: it can either take the place of demonstration, so that we use probable reasons instead of actual ones, or it can help our mind accept the following as demonstrations.[48] In ethics and politics, the proportions of dialectics can be called demonstrations on the grounds of similarity of subject matter. Thus dialectics is not only preparation for future demonstrations or confirmation of previous ones, but it can replace demonstrations when we are unable to form them[49] What is notable in this replacement, is that it does not occur in the theoretical sciences. Zabarella only allows dialectics to be used in place of demonstration in the practical disciplines.

At the end of his *De natura logicae* Zabarella discusses the roles of rhetoric and poetry as logical disciplines. There are three basic questions as to the nature of these disciplines. Firstly, on what grounds can rhetoric and poetry be considered logical disciplines? Secondly, which one is the end of poetry: delight or utility? Thirdly, what is the proper subject matter of poetical treatises: true facts, fictive stories or something else? These questions were fundamentally important for Zabarella and other sixteenth-century writers who discussed the proper place of rhetoric and poetry in the hierarchy of arts and sciences.

Lisa Jardine has maintained that the principal idea of the whole humanist logic was that an argument can be convincing even if it is not formally valid. The consequences of this are that formal validity is no longer the criterion of an argument, and demonstrative inference has no supremacy over non-demonstrative inferences.[50] Humanist writers even found it more

---

48  Zabarella 1597, 72e–73d.
49  Zabarella 1597, 80d–e.
50  Jardine L, CHRP 1988, 175–180.

proper to call the whole discipline of logic dialectics. The commentators on Aristotle's *Rhetoric* and *Poetics* at Padua, however, were influenced by the Aristotelian concept of science which prevailed at the university, so that, unlike Lorenzo Valla, Rudolf Agricola or Jean Luis Vives, these Paduan writers emphasized the demonstrative inference as proper for the speculative sciences.

A new interest in Aristotle's poetical theory arose at Padua in 1530's. *Poetics* was known in the Latin West from the thirteenth century, but it was not much used or commented upon. This is in part explained by the fact that the text available was distorted and not very easily interpreted.[51] A new "discovery" of Aristotle's *Poetics* began in 1498, when Giorgio Valla translated the book into Latin from Greek; although the standard version of the sixteenth century became Alessandro de Pazzi's edition of the Greek text of *Poetics* with a Latin translation, which appeared in 1536.[52]

A humanist literary academy, *L'Accademia degli Infiammati*, was founded at Padua in 1540, and many of its founder members, like Alessandro Piccolomini, Sperone Speroni, Bernardino Tomitano and Benedetto Varchi, wrote commentaries on Aristotle's *Poetics* and other works, in which they discussed the nature and place of rhetoric and poetry in the classification and hierarchy of different disciplines.[53] Poetry was usually absorbed in a rhetorical culture that emphasized the active life instead of pure contemplation.

As regards rhetoric and poetry, Zabarella's debt to these former members of *L'Accademia degli Infiammati* is obvious. Another major source for Zabarella's ideas is Averroes' paraphrasis of Aristotle's *Rhetoric* and *Poetics*; the influence of which on the

---

51  On these medieval translators and commentaries, see Aguzzi™Barbagli 1988, 153 (note 118).

52  Baxter Hathaway has declared that the sixteenth–century Italians can be said to have invented the *Poetics* of Aristotle, see Hathaway 1952, 4–5. On the "invention" of *Poetics* in the sixteenth century, see Aguzzi-Barbagli 1988, 108–110 and Vickers 1988, 718. On the reception of *Poetics* in the Latin West, see Tigerstedt 1968.

53  Bruni 1967; Cerreta 1957b; Doglio 1977, 55–64 and Vasoli 1968, 262–292. Referring to Sperone Speroni, Lionello Sozzi claims that the sixteenth century writers on rhetoric saw it increasingly as an artificial means of persuasion. On this point see Sozzi 1981, 67–69.

interpretation of *Poetics* was still notable in the middle of the sixteenth century.[54] According to him, rhetoric, which is similar to topics and part of logic, is made of eloquence and moral disciplines, above all politics.[55] In their commentaries on Aristotle's *Poetics*, both Avicenna and Averroes link poetry with rhetoric, and state that both these are parts of logic and, at the same time, instruments for moral disciplines.[56]

Bartolomeo Lombardi began to lecture on Aristotle's *Poetics* at the University of Padua in 1540's, but he died soon afterwards. Vincenzo Maggi wrote a preface to Lombardi's posthumously published commentary on Aristotle's *Poetics*, in which Maggi classified rhetoric and poetics as parts of logic, even if they do not use demonstration.[57] Francesco Robortello draws the same

---

54  Weinberg 1961, 352–361.
55  Averroes, *In libros Rhetoricum Aristotelis Paraphrases*, in *Aristotelis Opera cum Averrois commentariis* 1550, vol.II, f.31r: "Haec itaque ars est composita ex arte eloquentiae et ex arte morali, hoc est Politica ... Haec ergo ars est pars artis Logicae, quae similis est Topicae ..."
56  Nowhere in his works did Aristotle himself explicitly state that rhetoric and poetry were logical disciplines. In *Rhetoric* 1359b9–11, however, he writes that "rhetoric is a combination of the sciences of logic and of ethics; and it is partly like dialectic, partly like sophistical reasoning". Also at the beginning of *Rhetoric* Aristotle states that the technical study of rhetoric is concerned with the modes of persuasion, and persuasion is a sort of demonstation. Having considered the role of poetry in *Poetics* and *Rhetoric*, Butterworth comes to the conclusion that "it is fair to infer that Aristotle considers poetry to be a part of logic". Perhaps this conclusion is still too hasty and stems from Butterworth's intention to make Averroes' interpretation of *Poetics* as Aristotelian as possible. See Butterworth 1986, 14. On the logical character of poetry among Arab writers, see Hardison 1970, 59–61; Dahiyat 1974, 12–58; Halliwell 1986, 290–291 and above all Black 1990, 180–242. On the reception of Aristotle's *Poetics* both in Arab tradition and in Latin West, see *Medieval Literary Theory and Criticism* 1988, 277–288 and Black 1990.
57  *Vincentii Madii et Bartholomaei Lombardi in Aristotelis librum De Poetica communes explanationes* 1550, 8: " ... Nunc Poeticam, quam ille nominatim indicat, de qua non dubitatur, logicam pono. Et hoc cum reliquis illis aliis Demonstrativa scilicet, Dialectica, Sophistica, Rhetorica habere commune dico, quod neque materiae loco res habeant: verba tantum et orationem ... Rhetorica, Poeticaque, contra: quod non adeo vere ac proprie Logicae appellantur, neque syllogismo fere, sed exemplo atque enthymemate, rationibus quasi popularibus utuntur. Atque harum qua huiusmodi sunt, extant opera, orationes atque poemata, plurimumque in politicis occupantur argumentis ..." On Maggi (1498–1564) see Lohr 1978, 551–553. On Lombardi (died in 1541) see Lohr 1978, 543.

conclusion; that there are five faculties or disciplines which deal with discourse: demonstration, dialectics, rhetoric, sophistic and poetry.[58] As we can see from the works of Angelo Tio[59] and Bernardino Tomitano[60], it was common among these Paduan writers to consider rhetoric and poetry as part of logical disciplines.[61]

Zabarella took at face value the close connection between rhetoric and poetry on one hand and moral disciplines on the other. Even if rhetoric and poetry were instruments of philosophy, it would not make them directly part of logic; however, Zabarella considers them as part of particular logic. When the mode of argument lies in universal logic, rhetoric and poetry teach a specific use of argument applied to specific material. Rhetoric teaches the valid persuasion of all arguments under discussion. The rhetoricians have neglected the proper arguments of their discipline and instead have concentrated on such external elements as eloquence and touching people's minds, which do not contribute to the good goverment of a city-state. According to Zabarella, argumentation is the proper nature of rhetoric, and its

---

58  Robortello, *In librum Aristotelis de arte Poetica explicationes* 1548, 1: "Subiicitur tanquam materies poeticae facultati oratio, sicuti et aliis omnibus, quae circa orationem versantur. Eae aytem sunt quinque numero, Demonstratoria, ... dialectice, rhetorice, sophistice, poetice ... Omnes has subiectam sibi habent orationem." On Lombardi/Maggi's and Robortello's discussion on the nature of poetry see Miesen 1967. On the life and works of Robortello (1516–1567) see Lohr 1980, 693–695.

59  Tio, Angelo, *Quaesitum et praecognitiones libri Praedicamentorum Porphirii* 1547, f.20v: "Quomodo autem Poetica sit est instrumentaria, nec ars, nec scientia, nec virtus, sed pars logices eiusdem argumentis de facili concludetur, quibus et rhetorica huiusmodi."

60  Bernardino Tomitano, *Contradictionum solutiones in Aristotelis et Averrois dicta in primum librum Posteriorum Resolutiorum*, in *Aristotelis Opera cum Averrois commentariis* 1562, vol.I,3, 39r: " ... At hoc in loco per artes logicas non rationales facultates, sed sermocinatrices intelligit. Sic enim commune nomen est, Dialecticae, Demonstrativae, Sophisticae disciplinae, Grammaticam, Rhetoricae, atque Poeticae. Nam cum hae, omnes sermone utantur, logicae omnes vocantur, nomine hoc communi. Sunt autem sex, ut praecedens enumeratio colligit ...". See also Weinberg 1961, 4–7; Vasoli 1968, 294–296.

61  Halliwell's discussion on the sixteenth–century commentators of *Poetics* is the best description I have seen of the impoverished reading of *Poetics* in general. See Halliwell 1986, 293–301.

application to eloquence and emotion is the result of the corrupt habits of the citizens.[62] Thus Zabarella underlines the wholly intellectual nature of rhetoric in place of its eloquent or emotional nature.

In Zabarella's view rhetoric was formed from both logic and politics: from logic it acquired a mode of argument and from politics came its subject matter. The subject matter of rhetoric is all human action, whereas dialectics unconditionally discusses all possible matters.[63] The principal difference between these disciplines, however, lies in their ends: dialectics aims at cognition; rhetoric, as an instrument of politics, aims at action.[64] So, in a strict sense, rhetoric cannot be an instrument of the sciences, but only of practical disciplines and is properly only an instrument of politics.[65]

Poetics, however, does not consider any formal mode of argument, but adapts different people's habits and states of mind. Poetics teaches by example (*exemplum*), which is itself an uncomplete induction, as Aristotle states in *Posterior Analytics*. Human actions are singular matters and thus an example has a more eminent role than induction in practical disciplines, because induction is aiming at universal knowledge.[66] The art of poetics deals with examples, which teach how to imitate people's habits and actions and how to write poems; poems, in turn, clarify people's minds. The only thing that poetics adopts from universal logic is the method of example; nevertheless it is part of logic, because example is a mode of argument and an instrument which is applicable to all branches of logic. In order to gain knowledge by demonstration, all obstacles and confusions must be cleared up.

---

62  Zabarella 1597, 85e–87a.
63  Zabarella 1597, 90b–c.
64  Zabarella 1597, 89b: "Hac igitur differentia constituta inter eas duas facultates, quod una cognitionem respicit, altera actionem, manifestum est, ex ea una tanquam ex fonte reliquas omnes derivari."
65  Zabarella 1597, 88e–f: "Preaterea si vult orator persuadere auditoribus, ut aliquid agant, debet propositiones assumere eis cognitas, quia ex ignotis nulla sit persuasio. Ideo propositiones accipit in rebus agendis et in materia civili, non in materia naturali vel mathematica; iudex enim scientiarum ignarus esse existimatur. At Dialecticus, quum aptus esse debeat ad disputandum cum omnibus tam ignaris, quam eruditis in qualibet disciplina, nulli certae materia est addictus, sed in omnibus aeque versatur."
66  Zabarella 1597, 95b–c.

2

A person engaged in politics attempts to do this by means of rhetoric and poetry.[67]

Zabarella then asks the question, why did not Aristotle include rhetoric and poetry in his logical works (*Organon*), if they are parts of logic? He answers that they are not proper instruments of knowledge as are the three other parts of particular logic, and thus they do not belong to *Organon*.[68] According to Zabarella, the order of works on logic in *Organon* followed that found in classical Greek codex which was indeed the best one. Having first read *Ethics* and *Politics,* a person engaged in civic matters could put his political knowledge to instrumental use, assisted by those elements of rhetoric and poetry, which are appropriate to the administration of a city-state.[69]

Zabarella is at pains to show how rhetoric and poetry actually are parts of logic, and he thus underlines their argumentative character. He was well aware of the sixteenth-century tendency to define eloquence and persuasion as central parts of rhetoric. He does admit their use in the discipline of rhetoric, but claims that they are external to its nature.[70] On the other hand, when Zabarella emphasizes the argumentative nature of rhetoric, he has difficulty in separating it from dialectics, especially when Aristotle stressed the similarity between these disciplines in the second chapter of the first book of *Rhetoric*.[71] Zabarella claims that Aristotle meant here some sort of similarity between sentences. He admits that even a dialectician can use political material, but only as political knowledge not for any action in the meaning of rhetoric. According to him, persuasion and the verb persuade (*persuadere*), which belongs only to rhetoric, refer to action.[72] As we have seen,

---

67  Zabarella 1597, 96a–97d.
68  Zabarella 1597, 92c–d.
69  Zabarella 1597, 98e–99a.
70  Zabarella 1597, 86f: "Quare apud Aristotelem sola argumentatio naturam oratoriae artis constituit; affectionum autem commotio ab ipsa penitus aliena est, licet in usu sit propter mores civitatum corruptos; elucutio autem est saltem accidentaria et secundarie respicitur."
71  Aristotle, *Rhetoric* 1356a25–35.
72  Zabarella 1597, 92b–92d: "Aristoteles autem ipsam discrepantiam non declarat, quia de sola similitudine loquitur, ut naturam Rhetoricae declaret. Atqui certum est ea, quae ita proportione et analogia similia sunt, essentia ac definitione unum esse non posse. Non potest igitur definitione Rhetoricae

however, some pages earlier he had claimed that persuasion was only an external feature of rhetoric.

This difficulty stems in part from Zabarella's definition of logic. As we have seen, he wanted to restrict logic principally to the realm of the speculative sciences, not to the practical disciplines. He has to stress the argumentative and instrumental character of rhetoric because it is a part of logic; but on the other hand he has to admit that the end of rhetoric is action, so that it can be distinguished from dialectics, which only aims at cognition. Thus he comes to the conclusion that, as far as the form of rhetoric and poetry is concerned, they belong to logical disciplines, but when their end is under consideration, they differ from proper logic.[73] At the end Zabarella is trying to escape from this difficulty by claiming that while logical disciplines are primarily instruments of science and aim at knowledge, they can, as a secondary function, aim at action, too. On this ground, rhetoric and poetry, which aim at action as their ultimate end, can be counted as logical disciplines.[74]

---

Dialecticam complecti, nisi reprehensione digna ac vitiosa sit. Hac itaque responsione reiecta ego dicendum puto, per verbum (*persuadere*) distingui Rhetoricam a Dialectica; proinde dialecticam sub illa definitione non contineri, quoniam in illo verbo insita est vis quaedam, quae actionem respiciat. Dicimus enim alicui esse persuasum, quando ea ductus est ut ita agere velit. Dialecticum vero disputantem non dicimus velle adversario persuadere, quia non vult eum hortari ut agat, sed dicimus velle vincere vel opinionem quandam rei in eius animo gignere. Itaque persuadere est efficaci oratione ad agendum compellere, quod oratoris est proprium et Dialectico non convenit."

73 Zabarella 1597, 99d: "Ad hoc dubium respondere possumus, has duas disciplinas esse logicas ratione formae logicae, sed ratione finis aliquantum a natura logicae recedere et ab eius scopo deviare."

74 Zabarella 1597, 99f: "Sed rem diligentius ac profundius considerantes, dicimus has duas disciplinas etiam fine logicae participare. Logica namque instrumenta secundum proprian naturam verum a falso distinguunt et cognitionis instrumenta sunt; quo fit, ut quomodocunque iis utamur, semper cognitionem aliquam pariant primario. Deinde secundario et per cognitionem mediam actioni vel etiam effectioni inservire possint." Also ibid. 100b–c: "Hac igitur ratione hae duae disciplinae natura ac definitione logicae participant, quemadmodum et aliae. Omnes enim instrumenta logica propter cognitionem tractant, quae est eorum effectus proximus, licet aliquae cognitionem hanc ad actionem tanquam finem ultimum dirigant."

## 3.4. Poetry and moral instruction

As we have seen, the Arab writers based their interpretation of the moral aspect on poetry on their reading of Aristotle's *Poetics* and *Rhetoric*. It is, however, a moot point how far Aristotle himself stretched the moral aspect of poetry. In other words, did he see poetry as a means of moral education or did he consider it mainly as a fountainhead of delight? The latter interpretation, which sees poetry mainly as an aesthetic discipline and separated from all ethical or moral questions, has dominated research up to our own century.[75]

During the last few decades, a new interpretation of *Poetics* has gained ground in English speaking countries.[76] Stephen Halliwell has emphasized the need to locate *Poetics* in the context of

---

75 For example Butcher wrote in his book about *Poetics* that "the object of poetry, as of all the fine arts, is to produce an emotional delight, a pure and elevated pleasure ... We hear nothing of the ethical influence which the several kinds of poetry exert on the spectator or the reader, or of the moral intention of the poet." He also states that Aristotle "never allows the moral purpose of the poet or the moral effects of his art to take place of the artistic end. If the poet fails to produce the proper pleasure, he fails in the specific function of his art." Butcher 1898, 219,235. In his short history of aesthetics, Beardsley also claims that when Aristotle "turns to the art of poetry (poietike), he is determined to mark out boundaries and study the nature of that art quite independently of its moral and political connections". Beardsley 1966, 55. Likewise in his recent interpretation of the *Poetics* James Hutton has written that it "presents an idea of poetry that does not differ from Plato's: it is an imitation of human life; it aims at emotional pleasure, not moral instruction." Hutton 1982, 20.

76 Isaiah Smithson has explored the moral values of *Poetics* and Martha Nussbaum has discussed the moral values Aristotle sets upon tragedy. Smithson 1983; Nussbaum 1986, 378–394. Some Renaissance commentators seems to have been more sensitive than most of modern scholars to the "fragility of goodness", which Nussbaum emphasizes in her study. For example Alessandro Piccolomini wants to warn us as spectators of tragedy to see, "how easily man can fall from the peak of good fortune to the lowest state of misery, and how unstable and frail are the goods and pleasures of this life." Piccolomini 1572, 103: " ... posiach·ä· veggendo noi nei tragici avvenimenti, quanto agevolmente di sommo grado di fortuna, all'infimo si precipiti et quanto fallaci et fragili siano i beni et li contenti di questa vita, veniamo a temperare l'amore delle cose care; accioch·ä· la perdita di quelle, che cos·ç· facilmente poter'accascare, ci fa conoscer la tragedia, non ci habbia occorrendo, da perturbare et d'affligger tanto." Translated by F.V.Cerreta in Cerreta 1957a, 161.

Aristotle's philosophy as a whole, rather than as a separate theory of "the fine arts" based only on an isolated reading of *Poetics*.[77] After all, passages dealing with tragedy are not the only places where Aristotle has ethical value judgments in mind.[78] Moreover, if *Poetics* is read alongside *Rhetoric* and *Nicomachean Ethics*, as Halliwell does in his study, the picture becomes even clearer.[79]

The aesthetic interpretation of Aristotelian poetical theory was also dominant among scholars dealing with the sixteenth-century commentaries on *Poetics*. They separated moral values from his poetical theory, and implied that Aristotle's commentaries as well as Aristotle himself saw delight as poetry's chief end. In recent years some scholars have noted, however, that the instrumental value of rhetoric and poetry for moral disciplines increased, rather than decreased, during the century.[80] It is against this shift of interpretation that the sixteenth-century Paduan commentators

---

77  Halliwell 1986, 3–6. According to Halliwell this willingness to treat poetics as a separate treatise is partly based on an incorrect reading of chapter 25, where Aristotle states that "there is not the same kind of correctness in poetry as in politics, or indeed any other art." (*Poetics* 1460b14–15). In Halliwell's view this is not to be read as a declaration of the complete autonomy of poetic standards and principles. "What Aristotle does assert, against Plato, is that poetry should not be subjected to simple and direct evaluation in terms of external criteria – moral, political or otherwise ...but to grant this degree of independence is not to claim or establish the exclusion of ethical and other values from poetry; the passage from *Poetics* 25 denies the identity of poetic and moral criteria, but it does not state that they are wholly unconnected." Halliwell,ibid, 4.

78  For example, in the second chapter he states that "the objects the imitator represents are actions, with agents who are necessarily either good men or bad – the diversities of human character being nearly always derivative from this primary distinction, since it is by badness and excellence men differ in character. It follows, therefore, that the agents represented must either be above our own level of goodness, or beneath it, or just as we are." Aristotle, *Poetics* 1448a1–5. Aristotle goes on to say that comedy represents men as worse than they are; tragedy as better. This was interpreted later in the Middle Ages to mean that tragedy is the "art of praise" and comedy "the art of blame". On this point, see *Medieval Literary Theory and Criticism* 1988, 283–284.

79  On the relationship between rhetoric and moral disciplines in Aristotle's philosophy, see the recent considerations by Cooper (forthcoming) and Engberg–Pedersen (forthcoming).

80  Halliwell 1986, 317; Vickers 1988b, 736. In 1979 Paul Oskar Kristeller wrote that the emphasis in rhetoric shifted from persuasion to style and imitation. In 1983 he pointed out the relationship between rhetoric and moral disciplines, but did not deal with the instrumental character of rhetoric for ethics and politics. See Kristeller 1979, 251 and 1983, 17–18.

ought freshly to be considered. As we shall see, the separation of poetry and moral factors was not a general feature among commentators on *Poetics*. Naturally there are some individual writers, like Castelvetro and Riccoboni, who stressed the aesthetic dimensions of poetical theory, but this was not the general case.[81]

In the sixteenth century there were some tendencies to unite Horace's *Ars poetica* with the ideas expressed in Aristotle's *Poetics*.[82] At the beginning of the century Agostino Nifo had already defined rhetoric and poetry as parts of instrumental logic. Rhetoric is useful for public speeches and the aim of poetry is both to delight and to be useful, as Horace had said.[83] Also Zabarella refers to Horace's dictum of delight and utility as the ends of poetry; but considers these as hierarchically arranged, delight following utility, which it subserves. Thus the independent and

---

81  In 1570 Lodovico Castelvetro presented the most elaborated view on the behalf of the aesthetic reading of Aristotle's *Poetics*. He writes: "Poetry was invented for the pleasure of the ignorany multitude and the common people, and not for the pleasure of the educated ... Poetry was invented exclusively to delight and to give recreation." Castelvetro, *Poetica d'Aristotele vulgarizzata et sposta* 1570, I: 46,345. Cited from Aguzzi–Barbagli 1988, 115; translation by Danilo Aguzzi–Barbagli. Aguzzi–Barbagli analyses Castelvetro's interpretation in the following way: "Castelvetro drastically reduces the pedagogic potentials of the poetic language so strongly defended by the humanistic culture of the fifteenth century and abandons the moralistic concerns of the previous commentators in Latin on the ùPoeticsú." Victoria Kahn has also distinguished "the humanist conception of the morally educative activity of reading from the aesthetic conception of reading." Kahn 1985, 44. She claims that these two ways of reading were not so far apart as often has been assumed and notes "that when pleasure is given a role independent of ethics in the experience of reading, humanism has come to an end." Ibid, 205 (note 42). Perhaps Kahn is right here in regard to the end of humanism, but it does not disprove the fact that at least from 1570's there were commentators on Aristotle's *Poetics*, such as Castelvetro, who distinguished these two "ways of reading". Kahn seem to base her conclusions more on the fifteenth-century than the sixteenth-century works on rhetoric and poetry.

82  On Horace and his *Ars poetica*, see Brink 1971. On the reception of Horatian poetical theory in the sixteenth century see Aguzzi-Barbagli 1988, 103–107. On the fusing of Horatian and Aristotelian themes see Herrick 1946.

83  Nifo, *Prima pars opusculorum* 1535, 89: " ... Rhetorica licet moralis philosophiae sit instrumentum, ut Analytica naturalis philosophiae. Tamen utilis est in omnibus dicendi generibus, in quibus dicere solemus coram auditoribus. Poetica autem inventa est (ut Aristoteles auctor est in eo Libro, quem de poetica scripsit) et ad delectandum et ad conferendum quod Oratius affirmat, cum dicit: Et prodesse volunt et delectare poetae." See Weinberg 1961, 4.

proper end of poetry is not delight, but to give benefit by correcting manners and refreshing the soul. It may be appropriate to connect amusement to poetry in order to encourage people towards it, but when you aim only at amusement, you misuse the art of poetry.[84] This connection of amusement and utility was a common topic amongst the sixteenth century commentaries on *Poetics*, but Zabarella differs from most of them by laying special emphasis on the utility of poetics at the expense of amusement. While not denying the utility of poetics, writers like Robortello had stressed the delight poetry brings through the means of imitation.[85]

According to Zabarella, rhetoric and poetry are rather instruments of doing rather than contemplation, because the subject matter of these disciplines is suitable for action.[86] Having eliminated all other possible disciplines, he comes to the conclusion that either rhetoric and poetry are useful as instruments of politics, or they are not useful at all. Rhetoric and poetry are for him instrumental facuities which a citizen uses in action, that is to produce good citizens. There is the difference, however, that a person uses the art of rhetoric for himself, but poetry for others.[87] In Zabarella's view, rhetoric and poetry can be used either to produce good or bad results; however he sees the latter as misuse, because the proper end of rhetoric is to persuade people to justice.[88]

---

84  Zabarella 1597, 84c–e: "Ideo recte poeta dixit (Et prodesse volunt et delectare poetae). Quod ita intelligendum est, ut praecipue spectetur utilitas; delectatio secundario et propter utilitatem, non propter se. Quoniam autem in poematibus delectatio cum utilitate est commiscenda, hinc factum est, ut multi arte Poetica abutentes, poemata componerent, quae delectationem absque ulla utilitate praeberent; hi namque adulterini poetae praetermisso praecipuo huius artis scopo secundarium solum respiciunt, qui per se et sine altero quaerendus non esset."

85  Robortello, *In librum Aristotelis de arte Poetica explicationes* 1548, 2: "Poetice, siquis diligenter attendat, omnem suam vim confert ad oblectandum et si prodest quoque ... Quem igitur alium finem poetices facultatis esse dicemus, quam oblectare per repraesentationem, descriptionem et imitationem omnium actionum humanarum; omnium motionum; omnium rerum tum animatarum, tum inanimatarum?" See also Weinberg 1961, 388–390.

86  Zabarella 1597, 79b–c.

87  Zabarella 1597, 82f.

88  Aristotle makes the same distinction in *Rhetoric* 1355a31, where he notes that we must not make people believe what is wrong.

Zabarella's use of rhetoric and poetry expressly as instruments of the political art was not a unique idea among Paduan writers. In his vernacular annotations to Aristotle's *Poetics,* Alessandro Piccolomini had made the same claim about the use of poetical faculty. Poetry is nothing else than an imitation, but in this imitation it is not enough to imitate natural or artificial things; you have to imitate human actions, characters and passions if you really want to write poetry. The end of poetry is to give pleasure and ultimately, by giving it, to benefit human life.[89] According to Piccolomini, by imitating and praising virtous men we try to became like them. On the other hand, when we hear vices and wicked actions expressed through poetic imitation, we immediately hate, and try to avoid these vicious actions.[90] This is the way poetry serves the art of politics, in Piccolomini's view.

William Edwards has criticized Zabarella's treatment of these disciplines. According to Edwards, Zabarella saw only the cognitive part of these disciplines and failed to recognize their essential, aesthetic dimension.[91] In my view Edwards is trying to read Zabarella through humanist spectacles. Zabarella did not deny pleasure and aesthetic value, but maintained that these things cannot and should not be the basic goal and the principal end of rhetoric and poetry. An emphasis on the cognitive functions of these disciplines is a consistent result of his view of the nature of all logical disciplines. Moreover, as we have seen, in the question of the logical character of rhetoric and poetry, even the

---

89  Piccolomini, *Alessandro, Annotationi nel libro della Poetica d'Aristotile* 1575, proem (without pagenumbers): Poesia non sia altro, che imitatione non solo di cose, ò naturali, ò artifitiose; ma principalmente d'attioni, di costumi et d'affetti humani ... à fine di dilettare et dilettando finalmente giovare alla vita humana ... Et in cosi fatte imitationi si finisse et si terminasse, senza inserirle et applicarle et farle servir' all'imitatione di qualche attion dell'huomo; non potrebber questi imitationi propriamente et legittimamente attribuir' à se il vero nome di poesia." See also Weinberg 1961, 10–11,543–545; Aguzzi–Barbagli 1988, 118–119.
90  Ibid: "Con l'imitation degli huomini virtuosi et con la spressione delle lodi loro, veniamo ad infiammarci et ad escitarci alla virtù, per divenir simili ·Ö· quelli, che celebrar' udiamo. Se i vitii et le scelleratezze dall'altra banda sentiamo con poetica imitation' esprimere et esprimendo vilipendere et vituperare; subito cominciamo a disporsi alla fuga et all'odio delle vitiosi attioni." On Piccolomini's theory of poetry in general see Cerreta 1957a.
91  Edwards 1969, 848,852.

humanistic circles at Padua were more or less in accord with Zabarella's view.

Where these literal writers of Accademia degli Infiammati differed from Zabarella, however, was in their opinion that other kinds of logical inferences are not lower in rank to demonstrative reasoning. They considered that different disciplines have different ends and so use different means of argument.[92] Zabarella did not rank rhetoric and poetry very highly in the hierarchy of disciplines. The reason for this was that he was not very interested in subjects which were of no use to natural philosophy and other theoretical sciences. The demonstrative part of logic, which Aristotle dealt with in his *Analytics*, is the core of the whole discipline for him. Dialectics and topics are something of less importance, and rhetoric and poetry are even lower in the hierarchy of logical disciplines. Only with demonstrative syllogisms can you reach the degree of necessity that the theoretical sciences demand. This led him even to characterize poetry as a insignificant and obscure part of logic, whereas the members of *L'Accademia degli Infiammati* praised it to the skies.[93]

Zabarella's low estimate of poetry in part stems from the material it uses. In his paraphrases of Aristotle's *Poetics* Averroes lists six faults of which poetry is guilty. The first of these is that poems imitate something that is impossible, whereas they should only imitate things that exist or at least things that are possible. In describing the second error Averroes compares poetry with painting. Their common fault is that they falsify imitation by adding something that cannot be, for example by picturing some

---

92  This comes perfectly clear, for example, in Sperone Speroni's distinction between philosophers and orators. See Vasoli 1968, 268–270.

93  Zabarella 1597, 95d: "In utriusque instrumenti usu versatur rhetorica, ideo manifestissime logica est. Poetica vero quum omisso instrumento praecipuo usum alterius doceat, exigua et obscura logicae pars est." This statement of the value of *Poetics* can be compared with Maggi's and Lombardi's evaluation. Madii et Lombardi, *Aristotelis librum de Poetica communes explanationes* 1550, 11: "Huiusmodi poetica est, qualem diximus, Inflammati: nobilissima et antiquissima; iucundissima et nobis accommodatissima; sapientissima in poematibus, egregia in rebus omnibus, magistra vitae et dux ad humanam, divinamque felicitatem."

member of the body out of place.[94] During the sixteenth century poets were encouraged to deal with fables too, as in Robortello's commentary, where the fabulous was explicitly mentioned as the proper material for poetry; an opinion Zabarella shared.[95] On this ground, poetry approximates sophistry, which deals with false material. Nevertheless there are differences. The art of sophistry aims at cognition; poetry at action. Sophistry is wholly made for avoiding vice, whereas poetry teaches man both to avoid vice and imitate virtuous action, irrespective whether it is fact or fiction. In cognition, the result of accepting false propositions is ignorance; but in action, fictional material can just as well encourage the imitation of virtuous action as can fact.[96]

Like Zabarella's general definition of logic as an instrument mainly for the theoretical sciences, his emphasis on the usefulness of rhetoric and poetry and their linking with logic, was not unanimously approved at Padua. Antonio Riccoboni, who wrote commentaries on both *Poetics* and *Rhetoric*, criticized Zabarella's concept of poetry as being far too narrow. For Riccoboni, logic was not a part of science but an instrument useful for both theoretical

---

94 Averroes, *Paraphrasis in librum Poeticae Aristotelis*, in *Aristotelis Opera cum Averrois commentariis*, vol.II, 94r: "Sex sunt peccata, quae in poemate comittuntur, propter quae oportet poetam corripi. Primum est, quod imitetur id, quod est impossibile; quoniam imitatio debet esse de re, quae st, vel existimatur esse ... Secundum peccatum poetae est, ut falsificet imitationem. Ut pictor, qui addat in aliqua figura aliquod membrum, quod non habet, vel eam depingat in loco, in quo non debet esse." Averroes follows here the Aristotelian idea that every art has to imitate nature in the best possible way without changing anything or making any additions. This idea is under closer consideration in the chapter 5.

95 Robortello 1548, 1: "Ex his quaelibet facultas unum arripit genus, Demonstratoria verum. Dialectice probabile. Rhetorice suasorium. Sophistice id, quod probabilis, sed verisimilis habet speciem. Poetice falsum, seu fabulosum."

96 Zabarella 1597, 96e–f: "Nam et Poeta et Sophista in materia falsa versantur, siquidem ficta exempla a poeta proponuntur. Sed inter eas illud interest, quod quum Sophistica cognitionem, Poetica actionem respiciat. Ars Sophistica tota ad fugam est inventa, non ad usum; Poetica vero ad fugam et ad usum. In cognoscendis enim rebus non debemus illud credere, quod falsum est; et ex falsis propositionibus nulla fit cognitio, sed deceptio et ignorantia; tota igitur Sophisticae artis utilitas in fuga consistit, non in usu. At in agendo nihil refert an veras, an fictas actiones imitemur, modo bonae ac studiosae sint. Idcirco quum Poetica non cognitionem, sed actionem respiciat, sequitur ut, quamvis in materia falsa versetur, sit tamen et ad fugam et ad usum; pravas enim

and practical sciences.[97] Rhetoric and poetry, however, belong only partly to logic. Riccoboni agrees with Lombardi/Maggi and Zabarella that both disciplines use enthymemate and example, which are instruments of logic, and on this ground both can be included in logic. He disagrees, however, with Zabarella in the use of examples. According to Riccoboni, Zabarella claims that a poet uses examples in deeds, not in words. Riccoboni argues, Aristotle had said that all argumentation takes place in the words which express the things rather than in the things themselves. On this ground poetry cannot be included among logical disciplines.[98]

However, Riccoboni has not read Zabarella very closely on this point. He states explicitly that the words of poets are not arguments that would force people to good action, but rather signs, which express a person's habits and state of mind. The poets imitate these fictive habits and states of minds as examples in order to make people follow good deeds and avoid bad ones. Zabarella's intention here is not to demonstrate that poetry is a part

---

actiones fugere et bonas imitari bonum est, sive illae verae sint, sive fictae." In this point Alessandro Piccolomini, however, who earlier had also pointed out the moral value of poetry, differs from Zabarella's view. Piccolomini develops the theory of verisimilitude as the proper subject matter for poetical treatises. On this point see Cerreta 1957a, 146–150.

97  Riccoboni, *De usu Artis Rhetoricae Aristotelis commentarii* 1595, 71: "At Logica non propter se, sed propter aliud est, ut distinguat verum a falso in philosophia contemplandi et bonum a malo in philosophia agendi. Ergo non est pars, sed instrumentum philosophiae." See also Weinberg 1961, 582–584,603–608. On the life and works of Riccoboni (1541–1599), who was a professor of rhetoric at Padua, see Lohr 1980, 689–691.

98  Riccoboni, *Paraphrasis in Poeticam Aristotelis* 1587, 2: "At Bartholomeus quidem Lombardus, doctissimus Poeticae explicatur, eam excogitavit rationem, quod enthymemate et exemplo utatur, quemadmodum etiam Rhetorica. Quae ratio si probaretur, quominus omnes artes ad Logicam, tamquam partes referrentur, cum omnes enthymematis et exempli usum habeant. Profecto nihil esset impedimento, ut Jacobus Zabarella, Philosophus egregius, recte mea quidem sententia reprehendit. Altera ratio est Zabarellae ipsius, quod usum exempli non in verbis, sed in factis positi, doceat, cuius assumptum, ut is scriptum reliquit, a poeta proponitur, non verbis, sed factis. Consequens autem ipsi auditores et spectatores colligunt, quo ad bene agendum trahuntur. Quam ego rationem, libere ut dicam, quod sentio, magis viri indicare ingenium existimo, quam dubitationem eximere, ut propter huiusmodi argumentationem sic in mente conformatam et nulla oratione expressam, Poetica inter partes Logicae numeretur."

of logic, but only to separate the way orators and poets use example.[99]

According to Riccoboni, in both disciplines are many things that are not proper to logic, like habits and eloquence in rhetoric; characters, diction and harmony in poetry. In both disciplines, however, there is one aspect which ties them to logic. In rhetoric this is demonstrative discourse and in poetry, recognition (*agnitio*); which is made by syllogism or enthymeme. Recognition is the most beautiful part of plot (*fabula*) which, in turn, is the end of poetry, according to Riccoboni.[100]

Riccoboni also examines different opinions about the end of poetry. First he mentions Horace, whose definition combined delight and utility. According to Riccoboni, Zabarella preferred utility, to which he subordinated delight. Another sixteent-century commentator, Scaliger has most effectively stressed imitation as the end but, in Riccoboni's view, plot is the right end of the

---

99 Zabarella 1597, 95f–96a: "Alius est apud oratores, alius apud poetas exemplorum usus. Nam oratores verbo exemplis utuntur; poetae vero non verbo, sed re exempla ficta ob oculos spectantium ponunt, ut persuadeant bonos esse imitandos, pravos autem abhorrendos ac fugiendos. Itaque solum argumentationis assumptum a poeta proponitur non verbis, sed factis, consequens autem ipsi auditores et spectatores colligunt, quo ad bene agendum trahuntur. Poetarum vero et interlocutorum verba non sunt argumentationes, quae debeant alios hortari ad bene agendum, sed sunt signa indicantia personarum mores et affectiones, quas poeta imitatur, ut fictae illae affectiones et ficti mores et fictae actiones exempla sint, quae alii vel sequantur, vel fugiant."

100 Riccoboni, 1587, 87: "Iam constat Poeticam usum argumentandi tradere potissimum in agnitione et hoc modo Logicae partem esse. Nam, tametsi multa habet, quae ad Logicam non pertinent. Satis tamen est, ut in aliqua re praecipua appellari Logica queat, quemadmodum Rhetoricae quoque evenit, quae non solam continet oratoriam demonstrationem, propter quam ad Logicam redigitur; sed simul mores et affectus et praeterea elocutionem et partium dispositionem. Tamen Logicae pars dicitur propter unum demonstratione artificium. Sic Poetica, praeter sententiam, quam ei diximus esse cum Rhetorica communem, non unam pertractat fabulam, cuius praecipua pars, quae dicitur agnitio, syllogismo eget; sed mores quoque et dictionem et harmoniam et apparatum. Tamen propter unam ratiocinationem, quae fit in fabula, cuiusque usum docere ad ipsam potissimum spectat, videtur ab Averroe, maximo philosopho et ab aliis fuisse pars Logicae appellata." Terence Cave makes a mistake in claiming that, as against Riccoboni, Zabarella did not consider poetry as a part of logic at all. Apparently Cave's interpretation stems from his reading of Riccoboni, not Zabarella himself. Cave 1988, 73–74.

poetical faculty.[101] He explicitly denies Zabarella's definition of utility as the end of poetry, because it is a proper end of philosophy and concerns poetry only accidentally. Utility is therefore only an external end of poetry whereas, according to Riccoboni, delight in plot forms its internal and natural end. The construction of the plot has pleasurable consequences, and the utilitarian results are, in Riccoboni's view, only accidental.[102] Riccoboni was not the last Paduan professor to write an influential commentary on *Poetics*, however. His immediate successor Paolo Beni again emphasized the moral meaning of all poetical works.[103]

In the last chapter of his *De natura logicae* Zabarella deals with the question of the art of history, and its relationship to logic. A poem or a speech are not part of logic, but the arts of rhetoric and

---

101 Ibid,2: "Nam apud Horatium in epistola ad Pisones tres fines commemorantur, vel sola utilitas, vel sola delectatio, vel utilitas cum delectatione coniuncta ... Alii putant finem esse imitationem, alii fabulam. Primum autem finem Zabarella sic probavit, ut scripserit, scopum naturalem Poeticae esse utilitatem, atque adiectam esse delectationem, ut homines ad utilitatem percipiendam allicerentur."

102 Ibid,4–5: "Sequitur igitur, ut fabula sit finis totius poesis. Qui tametsi inferior esse finis videtur, ad alterum finem, nempe ad delectationem relatus ... et duplicem esse finem poeticae, unum naturale et insitum, id est fabulosam delectationem; alterum assumptum et extrinsecus proficiscentem, nempe utilitatem, quam poetae afferre conantur ut Politicae pareant, iubenti, ut prosint et minitanti, si aliter fecerint, se eos expulsuram. Quemadmodum etiam in Rhetorica duo sunt fines, unus naturalis, ut persuadeat, de quo nulla dubitatio est ... alter assumptus ex Politica, ut civitati persuadendo profit; quem Zabarella Rhetoricae tribuit communiter cum Poetica, scribens: Ad huiusmodi finem cum et ars Poetica et ars Rhetorica dirigantur, recte dictum videri, eas instrumenta esse, quibus homo civilis utitur ad bonos cives efficiendos. Egregie mea quidem sententia, si talis finis esse per accidens, alter per se intelligatur. Probat praeterea finem Poeticae esse utilitatem, ex Tragoediae definitione, ubi dicitur eam inducere perturbationum purgationem; quem finem ne nos quidem negamus, sed esse per accidens existimamus."

103 On the life of Beni (1552–1625) see Diffley 1988 and Lohr 1975, 266. Diffley tries to set Beni in his intellectual context and free him from the accusations of being a Baroque writer. However, Diffley has compared Beni only with some of his forerunners, which makes him exaggerate Beni's originality in some aspects of poetical theory. For example, in the question of verisimilitude, Diffley does not deal with Alessandro Piccolomini at all, even if Diffley knew that Beni owned a copy of Piccolomini's commentary (ibid, 188). Also for some reason he does not treat Zabarella's and Riccoboni's discussion on the nature of poetry. This leads Diffley to consider Beni's approach to the moral aspect of poetry too novel (ibid, 201).

poetry are. In the same way, not history itself, but the art of history should belong to logic. According to Zabarella, however, neither Aristotle nor anybody else has written this kind of book, and he doubts whether it would ever be worth writing. History consists of plain narration of past events, and there is no place in history for human thinking or invention. In fact, it is doubtful whether the phrase "art of history" can be used at all if there is no room for human will and if it is not man-made as are logical disciplines.[104]

For Zabarella, history is the plain narration of events with no other human artificial production than except, perhaps, eloquence which, as external and accidental for human beings is typical of history. Even those aspects of human artifice which can be perceived in history, are in fact parts of grammar, rhetoric or some other discipline. Since nothing man-made can be said to belong to the proper nature of history, it cannot be treated as an art. Even if the name "art" was granted to history, it would not then be a part of logic because it would not be used to explain other arguments; that is, it would not be an instrument. In Zabarella's view there can be no other parts of logic besides the ones already mentioned. Even grammar does not belong to proper logic.[105]

The classical background for Zabarella's condemnation of the art of history is the ninth chapter of *Poetics*, where Aristotle compares history with poetry. He explicitly denies the difference between poetry and history is between verse and prose. Instead he

---

104  Zabarella 1597, 100d–e: "Ars tamen historica non modo ab Aristotele, sed a nemine hactenus scripta comperitur, nec fortasse digna est, in qua scribenda tempus conteratur. Ea namque in simplici, ac nuda rerum gestarum narratione consistit; quo fit, ut nihil nobis fingendum, aut excogitandum relinquatur, ad quod facilius inveniendum praecepta de historia scribenda tradere, ac in artem redigere operae pretium fuerit. Ars enim non dicitur nisi eorum, quae a nostra voluntate pendent et aliquo humano artificio fabricantur, cuiusmodi est logica tota et quaelibet eius pars."

105  Zabarella 1597, 100f–101a: "At historia nil huiusmodi tractat, sed est nuda gestorum narratio, quae omni artificio caret; praeterquam fortasse elocutionis, quod quidem et alia eiusmodi quisque sanae mentis extranea et accidentaria ipsi historiae esse iudicaret. Quicquid enim artificii in historia notare potest, illud omne vel a Grammatica, vel a Rhetorica, vel ab alia aliqua arte desumptum est. Itaque si nullum humanum artificium in historia locum habet, quod eius proprium sit et ad eius naturam essentiamque pertineat, nulla certe ars de historia scribenda tradi potest ... Historica ars non datur; imo etiamsi daretur, logicae pars non esset, quia non in declarando alicuius argumentationis usu versaretur."

claims poetry is "something more philosophic and of graver import than history, since its statements are of the nature rather of universals, whereas those of history are singulars."[106] In Aristotle's view, history consists of things that have happened, but poetry of things that might happen; that is, that are possible by the standards of probability or necessity.[107]

Thus it becames obvious that Zabarella has imitated Aristotle in his comparison of these disciplines. What is interesting is that Zabarella has slightly changed the criteria of the invalidity of historical narrations. According to Aristotle, history cannot reach the universal abstraction needed in higher sciences, but he does not therefore condemn the whole subject on this ground. However, Zabarella denies human action has any role in historical narrations and thus he denies the value of the whole discipline. Moreover, his denial seems little harsh if we remember that Francesco Patrizi, for example, had written an art of history in the very manner which Zabarella had considered impossible, or at least not worth writing.[108]

Zabarella's general attitude towards humanism cannot be considered very favourable. He did not, however, openly criticize humanist writers and, of course, he himself used the textual criticism the humanist writers had developed. With the humanistically orientated Paduan commentators on *Rhetoric* and *Poetics* he also shared the view that these disciplines are useful for the moral education of citizens. Like Averroes and Alessandro Piccolomini before him, he thus stressed the instrumental utility of poetry for politics, and the didactic purpose of the whole discipline rather than any purely aesthetic values of delight and pleasure.

His general attitude towards logical disciplines was, however, quite different from the attitude of the humanists. Zabarella saw

---

106  Aristotle, *Poetics* 1451b5–7. On a detailed study of this chapter see G.E.M. de Ste. Croix 1975.

107  *Poetics* 1451a36–b1.

108  For the history of the "art of history" in Renaissance, see Cochrane 1981, 479–487; Diffley 1988, 206–209. As opposed to Zabarella, Paolo Beni considered history most useful for other arts and sciences. For him, history was not just a record of past events, but above all the teacher of prudence through example. Thus Beni placed a high moral value on history. See Diffley 1988, 210–211.

demonstrations and syllogisms that Aristotle had developed in the *Analytics* as the main part of logic, not dialectics or topics that the humanists preferred. Instead of probability, the certainty of syllogistic demonstrations was for him the core of scientific argument. Zabarella and the humanists had also different opinions about the role of rhetoric, poetry and history. The first two were for him parts of logic and of minor importance compared with the demonstrative logic presented in the *Analytics*. History he did not consider worth writing at all; which opinion differed radically from the views of the humanist writers.

# 4. The methodology of arts and sciences

## 4.1. Orders of presentation

As we have seen in previous chapters, Jacopo Zabarella made a clear-cut distinction between theoretical, and practical or productive disciplines. As a natural consequence he wanted to point out that this division had an implication for the methodology of different kinds of arts and sciences.[1] Zabarella deals with the nature of scientific method in his *De methodis* (On methods), which is the second major book in his *Opera logica*. At the beginning of this book he speaks about methods in the wide meaning of the term. Understood widely, methods are the habit of logic or the intellectual instrumental habit for acquiring knowledge of things.[2] Method can either be an instrumental habit; that is, not applied to any discipline; or it can be the discipline

---

1 After John Herman Randall's famous essay (Randall 1961) there has been a lively discussion of the methodology of these Paduan Aristotelians and its implication for modern science. This discussion, however, seems to be of a secondary importance to our present study and thus I deal with this it only where it seems appropriate. On the methodology of Paduan Aristotelians see besides Randall's essay Risse 1983; Papuli 1983; Crescini 1965; Edwards 1960,1967; Poppi 1969,1972; Gilbert 1963; Schmitt 1983b; Bottin 1972; Randall 1976 and N.Jardine 1976, the latter of which perhaps remains so far the best article written on this subject.

2 Zabarella 1597, 135a: "Haec igitur ample sumpta methodus nil aliud esse videtur, quam habitus logicus, sive habitus intellectualis instrumentalis nobis inserviens ad rerum cognitionem adipiscendam." Lisa Jardine has maintained that there are three distinct contexts for a discussion of method in classical

itself, where it is applied. According to Zabarella, Aristotle often called arts and sciences methods, because they all use methods and are formed by them.[3]

The subject of *De methodis*, however, is methods separated from matter. Methods in the wider meaning of the word can be divided into methods of presentation (*ordo, ordines*), and methods in the strict sense of the word (*methodus*). There is no reasoning involved in the first ones; they only arrange and order already existing knowledge. The task of proper method is not to arrange different parts of knowledge, but to infer the unknown from already known things. In the two first books of *De methodis* Zabarella speaks of orders of presentation; the two last books are about demonstrative reasoning methods.

In each discipline the order of presentation must be dealt with before proper methods. The teacher considers first the way the parts of the discipline must be presented, and only afterwards does he examine the methods of gaining knowledge of the individual parts. For example, in natural science all animals are first distinguished universally and then by individual species. From this universal examination is decided the nature of each species, if it is still unknown. The methods for arranging a body of knowledge are therefore wider than the proper methods. To organize a science, universal parts must be compared, whereas no form of

---

and Renaissance writing: "Firstly there is a discussion of axiomatic method, ultimately based on Euclid's *Elements* and Proclus' commentary on Euclid (first translated into Latin in 1560). Secondly there is the long-standing discussion of methods of demonstration, primarily based on Aristotle's *Posterior Analytics*, but often referring to Plato's theory of dialectic, Galen's remarks on method in the *Ars Parva* and Averroes' remarks in his commentary on Aristotle's *Physics*. Thirdly there is the discussion of methods for laying out available material for clarity, sometimes distinguished under the alternative term ordo, and based on sources which include those for the discussion of methods of demonstration, together with remarks in Cicero, Quintilian, and in the pseudo-Cicero's *Ad Herennium*." L.Jardine 1974, 28– 29. According to Jardine there was a marked tendency among the reforming dialecticians to confuse these contexts, and this was one of the bitterest criticisms levelled against them by competent orthodox Aristotelians like Zabarella. He was capable of keeping the contexts apart and of distinguishing between the different intended functions of the various types of ordering procedure. The basic study of the methodological concepts during the Renaissance remains still Gilbert 1960.

3 Zabarella 1597, 135b–d.

comparison is applied to method in the proper sense, which consists solely of investigation of some specific matter.[4] According to Zabarella, many former writers have maintained that the reasonable organization of all disciplines involves nothing more than following the order prevailing in nature. He himself does not, however, agree with this opinion, and says that the doctrinal order is the ordering principle of all disciplines, not the natural order.[5]

The aim of proper methods is knowledge, but the aim of the *ordines* is to learn things more easily and more thoroughly. In Zabarella's view those people err who claim that one and the same discipline can be taught in different ways, for example, according to teacher's choice. Every discipline has an ideal doctrinal order, without which it is difficult to achieve a complete knowledge of the facts.[6] Zabarella claims that Euclid and Aristotle said that every discipline must be arranged from the universal to the particular, because the knowledge of the particulars is dependent on the universals.[7]

In the second book of *De methodis,* Zabarella discusses the nature of the different kinds of orders for arranging a body of knowledge, and their natures. At the beginning of his *Ars medica* Galen distinguished three different orders of presentation: compositive, resolutive and definite. According to Zabarella, medical men who swear by Galen's name follow his doctrines blindly without investigating their contents rationally.[8] Zabarella himself rejects the definitive order as unnecessary and claims that there are only two orders of presentation: compositive and resolutive.[9]

These orders of presentation aim at two different kinds of knowledge. Either their end is knowledge for its own sake, as in the contemplative sciences, or it is knowledge which leads to action, as in all other disciplines. The arts also aim at knowledge,

---

4  Zabarella 1597, 138f–139e.
5  Zabarella 1597, 141c–144d. This subject led to a dispute between Zabarella and Francesco Piccolomini, who preferred the natural order also as an order of teaching. Piccolomini attacked Zabarella in his *Universa de moribus* (1583) and Zabarella answered him in his *Apologia de doctrinae ordine* (1584).
6  Zabarella 1597, 150f–153a.
7  Zabarella 1597, 157d–158a.
8  Zabarella 1597, 165e–166a.
9  Zabarella 1597, 176e.

but action is their primary and ultimate end. This dichotomy corresponds to the two different kinds of disciplines. When in the contemplative sciences you aim at scientific knowledge, it is necessary to start with compositive order from first principles in order to end up with complete knowledge. When you aim at action, however, you start with resolutive order from the ultimate end and move towards first principles in order to achieve the desired end. Contemplative sciences can never be arranged according to the resolutive order and, conversely, all the other disciplines only use the resolutive order.[10]

At the end of the second book of *De methodis* Zabarella makes a summary of these two kinds of orders of presentation. The compositive order is an instrument of logic by which all parts of a contemplative science are organized; so that from the first principles we move to the second ones, following the best and simplest order of presentation. Zabarella wants to emphasize that the compositive order has nothing to do with reasoning from one principle to another, but is only a presentation of parts of science; that is the necessary process from a greater universal to a less. In natural sciences, for example, this means the ordering of principles from genera to species.[11]

On the other hand the resolutive order is an instrument of logic where the end has been produced and generated by free men. Zabarella reminds us that action is always the ultimate end of the resolutive order. In every art there are two things under consideration: its end and its principles. From an universal and confused knowledge of the end, we proceed first to a common knowledge of principles and afterwards to a more specific and particular knowledge of these principles.

For example, if the end of the art of building is a house, then its principles are bricks, stones, timber and other materials. In every art the order of presentation is the beginning of action; for example when the art of building is examined, we move from the mental image of a house to a material house. The universal material qualities are first decided from the image of the house; that is, it must be strong, windtight and waterproof. Then, by examining

10 Zabarella 1597, 180c–181a.
11 Zabarella 1597, 214f–215c.

particular knowledge, we find bricks to be an appropriate material for the house.[12] In the same way Aristotle says, in his *Nicomachean Ethics*, that happiness is virtuous action and afterwards he examines the virtues, first universally and then in particular.[13]

Zabarella tries to answer an objection which has been made against this reasoning. If there is involved deliberation and reasoning in resolutive order, is it not rather a method than an order of presentation? Zabarella objects to this on two grounds. First he clears up the distinction between orders of presentation and methods by saying that there can be some kind of inference in resolutive order, but never in compositive one.[14] Zabarella himself prefers another answer, however. The resolutive order is necessarily connected to the method and for some grounds it can be called a method, for others an order. While working as a method it makes inferences, but while working as an order it only arranges different disciplines. According to Zabarella, even Averroes thought that the same process could sometimes be called a method, sometimes an order, on different grounds.[15] This passage shows that even for Zabarella himself the difference between a method and an order was not quite clear in arts.

Some writers tried to compare the different orders and place them in a hierarchy. Zabarella thinks that this is absurd, because every discipline has only one possible order of presentation. The only valid criterion for comparing these orders, therefore, is the nobility of the disciplines themselves. Because the contemplative sciences precede all other disciplines, the compositive order is more valuable than the resolutive one. The composite order is never deduced from the resolutive one, whereas the latter exists as

---

12  Zabarella 1597, 190d–192f. This resembles Aristotle's description of the process in arts at *Metaphysics* 1032a10–34b19. Aristotle's example here is the art of medicine, where the doctor proceeds from the end (health) to the proper principles in order to reach that end. On this Aristotle's passage see Gill 1989, 120–126.
13  Zabarella 1597, 216e–217c.
14  Zabarella 1597, 218a–218b.
15  Zabarella 1597, 218d–e: "Sic dicimus de ordine resolutivo; methodum enim necessario habet coniunctam et alia ratione dicitur ordo, alia ratione methodus. Facit quidem illationem, quatenus est methodus, cuius est proprium ratiocinari; at quatenus est ordo, nil aliud facit, quam dispositionem."

the end of the former. These are the reasons why the composite order can be considered to be more valuable than the resolutive one.[16]

## 4.2. Methods of demonstration

In the third book of *De methodis* Zabarella proceeds from the orders of presentation to methods in a stricter sense. For him these are intellectual instruments proceeding from the known to produce knowledge of the unknown. Such methods have argumentative force and deal with the specific problems of the disciplines instead of arranging the contents of a whole discipline, as do the orders of presentation.[17]

Zabarella distinguishes dialectics and dialectical syllogisms from proper methods, because the former are only like methods in form, but not in matter. He compares dialectics with a wooden sword which, materially, can be called a sword, but not in practice, until it can fulfil its function. A syllogism is the common genus and form of all methods and thus can be called a method. According to Zabarella, a syllogism is a formal method in which the whole argument must be presented. In his view all logical inferences can be reduced to induction and syllogism. Moreover, when it considers all the particulars of which the universal consists, even the complete induction can be reduced to a syllogistic form.[18]

In estimating the number of methods which exist Zabarella rejects the claims that there are four: demonstrative, resolutive, definite and divisive. Of these four, he accepts only the two first:

---

16  Zabarella 1597, 219f–220a.
17  Zabarella 1597, 224e–225f.
18  Zabarella 1597, 227f: "Inductio autem si perfecta sit, vim habet necessariam colligendi, sed per syllogismum; ea enim ratione concludit, qua vim syllogismi habet et ad bonum syllogismum redigi potest, ut ibidem declarat Aristoteles in capite de Inductione." Zabarella is right here, because Aristotle really considered complete induction a syllogistic form of inference. See *Posterior analytics* I, 2 and Kakkuri–Knuuttila and Knuuttila 1990, 296.

demonstrative method (*demonstratio propter quid, demostratio potissima*) and resolutive method (*demonstratio quia, syllogismus a signo*). Resolutive method proceeds from an effect to a cause, but demonstrative method, in contrast, from a cause to an effect. Induction is for him a subspecies of the resolutive method and, according to him, Aristotle does not introduce any other methods.[19]

Zabarella also rejects the claim that new definitions can be invented by the means of the method of division. In his view, only two kinds of things are naturally known. First, there are principles, which are immediately known and the most obvious. Secondly, come those things which are discovered after some consideration but without any intermediate step; such as axioms, definitions and suppositions. These are usually obvious to all students once a teacher has presented them. Knowledge known by nature need no further proof, but should be recognized as true immediately after it has been presented. The method of division can neither prove things known by nature, like the definitions of a circle or a man, nor anything that is completely unknown.[20]

In place of knowledge, division can be of use in presenting the different parts of a discipline. According to Zabarella, division is, both in the universal and particular sense, more a method of presentation than a method of demonstration. In a strict sense it is not even a method of presentation, but an instrument of such. By division we distinguish the different meanings of words and remove their ambiguity and, therefore, it is a servant of the instruments of logic. In his view, Aristotle had nothing against division other than that it has no syllogistic force. Zabarella finds it even easier to abandon the definitive method, because for him it is part of the method of division. Definition is the simple expression of an essence and marks no process from one thing to another. It cannot be a method, for it does not have the form that method requires.[21]

Every step from known things to unknown is either from an effect to a cause or from a cause to an effect. The former represents

---

19  Zabarella 1597, 230e–231a.
20  Zabarella 1597, 238a–239a.
21  Zabarella 1597, 244f–246e.

the resolutive, the latter the demonstrative (compositive) method. No other means of gaining knowledge exist according to Zabarella. The resolutive method is a servant of the demonstrative one. Resolution has no end in itself in the process of acquiring knowledge, but functions as the beginning of the compositive method. The ultimate end of a science is to proceed from the knowledge of principles to a complete knowledge of effects by means of the demonstrative method. If all principles are known, resolution is unnecessary. In this case the demonstrative method proceeds straight from the known principles to an effect, as in mathematics, where there is no place for resolution.[22] In fact, the resolutive method is used more in the natural sciences. Were the principles of all natural things self-evident, there would be no use for resolution even in the natural sciences. The end of the demonstrative method is complete knowledge, which means knowledge of things through their causes. The end of the resolutive method is more invention than knowledge. It seeks causes, the effects of which are later demonstrated by the compositive method.[23]

In a brief treatise called *De speciebus denmonstrationis* (On the species of demonstration) Zabarella considers the degree of necessity involved in resolution and composition. According to him, our mind thinks that the necessity in resolution is somehow weaker than the necessity in composition, even though it is, in fact, as strong. Even if we do not know something for sure in the necessity of resolution, we know enough of it for it to be called a syllogism.

Following Averroes, Zabarella distinguishes three different degrees of necessity in our cognition. In the first degree of necessity we know the necessity of a thing which has a cause by means of that cause; as, for example, we know human being to be laughing because he is rational. In the second degree of necessity we notice the necessity of a thing, but we do not know the cause of it; as when we know human being to be laughing without the knowledge of his rationality. In the third degree of necessity we know something to be always true, but that this is not essential for

---

22  Zabarella 1597, 265f–267a.
23  Zabarella 1597, 267c–d.

the thing. We know, for example, all ravens to be black, but while we recognize the universality of this accident in the subject matter, that is blackness of the ravens, we do not see anything in the ravens that would force them to be black.[24]

In this last case our senses keep on reminding us of the truth of the blackness of the ravens, but in spite of this our mind never comes quite convinced of their blackness and imagines a white raven. This happens because there is nothing essential in the connection between blackness and the ravens.[25] All the propositions used in resolution, however, are of either the first or second degree and, therefore, contain a quite high level of necessity. For example, even if we do not know how essentially human beings and laughter belong together, we know that this relationship must be essential because we cannot separate them factually or mentally. According to Zabarella, the third degree of necessity is not very high, but we do not have to rely on it in natural sciences because it does not represent such a certainty that is needed in scientific demonstrative propositions.[26]

At the end of the third book of *De methodis* Zabarella considers the question which disciplines really use methods. Proper

---

24  Zabarella 1597, 429d–e: "Primus gradus est, quando cognoscimus necessitatem rei habentis causam per cognitionem causae; ut quando cognoscimus, hominem esse risibilem propterea quod est rationalis. Secundus est, quando eandem eiusdem rei necessitatem cognoscimus absque cognitione causae; ut quando cognoscimus, hominem esse risibilem sine cognitione rationalitatis. Tertius gradus est, quando cognoscimus necessitatem propositionis de omni, quae non sit per se, ut omnem corvum esse nigrum; quia cognoscimus universitatem et perpetuitatem illius accidentis in illo subiecto, cuius nulla est causa, quae ad corvum quatenus corvus est, pertineat; quae quidem cognitio necessitatis admodum debilis est et parum certitudinis habet."

25  Zabarella 1597, 429f: "Quoniam etsi sensus videt, omnem corvum nigrum esse, mens tamen dicit, posse corvum non esse nigrum et album corvum cogitat; quia nulla est essentialis connexio nigredinis cum natura corvi."

26  Zabarella 1597, 430f: "Quare nullum novit intellectus essentialem connexum, quia nullus adest; et illius inhaerentiae, quae ex accidenti necessaria esse dicitur, non potest habere tantam certitudinem, quantam omnis demonstrativa propositio requirit." Jeroen van Rijen compares this passage with Zabarella's treatment of *de omni/per se* -distinction in his commentary on *Posterior Analytics* I,6. Van Rijen comes to the same conclusion that according to Zabarella necessities of this third type are of no use in scientific proofs and, perhaps, on second thought he denied their necessity altogether. See Zabarella 1597, 747b–748c and van Rijen 1989, 133–135. As a matter of fact Zabarella's interpretation on the type of necessity needed in natural sciences differed considerably from the view of nominalists. Scotus, Ockham

methods are employed in the contemplative sciences, which seek knowledge for its own sake. They are, therefore, instruments of the speculative sciences, assisting the perception of unknown things. The active and productive disciplines, which are concerned with contingent matter, do not aim at knowledge, and have no proper method or science or necessity. That necessity which they have is only necessity in proportion to their own ends (*ex suppositione finis*), not absolute (*simpliciter*) necessity.[27] This kind of inference can only be used in arts; in speculative sciences Zabarella denies the use of demonstrations *ex suppositione finis*.[28]

The methods do not really relate to artistic disciplines, although certain similarities do permit their application to the arts. The term science is only partially appropriate in such cases.[29] The process

---

and Buridan, for example, considered these first two types of necessities conceptual, but the third type natural, which, instead of the first two types, is used in natural sciences. On the view of the nominalists on natural necessity, see Knuuttila 1989b, 172–176 and Thijssen 1987, 252–255.

27  Zabarella 1597, 272b–c: "Quod quando de methodis loquimur, scientias contemplativas respicimus, quarum finis est scire. Methodi namque scientiam rerum ignotarum pariunt, quare scientiarum speculativarum instrumenta sunt. In his enim scientia proprie dicta locum habet, non in artibus et aliis operatricibus disciplinis, quae in rebus contingentibus versantur, et actionem, vel effectionem, non scientiam quaerunt. In his igitur proprie dicta methodus non datur, sicuti neque proprie dicta scientia, neque vera necessitas; si quam enim necessitatem habent, eam tantum habent, quae dicitur ex suppositione finis." The same idea is expressed in Zabarella 1597, 13b–d: "Quaelibet enim ars docens, ut aedificatoria et medica, sumit propositiones quasdam necessarias, ex quibus necessarias conclusiones colligit. Sed si bene consideremus, non est ibi necessitas simpliciter dicta, sed solum ex constitutione finis; aliquo enim fine constituto, caetera omnia ex eo colliguntur ... Tota igitur haec necessitas est ex finis constitutione, seu (ut dicitur) suppositione."

28  Zabarella 1597, 684a–b: "Scire enim aliquid ex suppositione alterius falsi, vel ignoti est nihil scire ... Sic etiam si prima principia sint incognita ...conclusiones ex eis deductae non scientur simpliciter et proprie, sed solum ex suppositione; si vera sunt illa principia, quae tamen ignorantur; hoc enim revera non est scire." William Wallace has dealt with the notion *ex suppositione finis* in Aristotelian tradition and in the thought of Galileo. See Wallace 1981a and 1981b. For a critique of Wallace's view on the similarity of Thomas Aquinas'and Buridan's views on this point, see Knuuttila 1989b, 173–174.

29  Zabarella 1597, 272d: "Quoniam igitur methodi sunt instrumenta acquirendi certam scientiam; ideo huiusmodi disciplinis proprie non competunt, aptari tamen illis aliquo modo possunt per similitudinem pro subiectae materiae conditione, quemadmodum etiam scientiae nomen improprie acceptum ipsis quandoque tribuitur."

from the end of an art to the reasoning of the principles really involves the resolutive method and is connected to a resolutive order of presentation rather than to a demonstrative process. In the art of medicine, for example, we can invent the remedies from what is already known about health and sickness. We use the term "invention" (*inventio*) and admit it to be a demonstration, which is a resolutive method. The method of demonstration cannot be called the invention of demonstration, because the term "invention" refers only to whether something exists, but the term "demonstration" refers to the question of why it exists. Thus the method of the art of medicine seems to return to resolutive rather than the demonstrative method.[30]

Zabarella dedicates the fourth and the last book of *De methodis* to questioning why Aristotle did not deal with orders of presentation in his books on logic. Zabarella distinguishes two reasons why Aristotle omitted the handling of orders from his work on logic. In the first place, he did not write his logic for teachers, for whom the ordering of disciplines is primarily relevant, but for students, for whom the knowledge of logical rules is more useful and even necessary. Secondly, Aristotle was sure that there are only two methods, compositive for the contemplative sciences and resolutive for operational disciplines. In the first book of the *Physics* Aristotle deals with compositive order, and in the seventh book of the *Metaphysics* with the resolutive one. The qualities of both orders of presentation are explained in these passages and so, according to Zabarella, there was no need for a specific book about them.[31]

This question apparently presents Zabarella with some difficulty, because he is convinced that Aristotle himself really created the division between orders and methods. If we assume, as

---

30 Zabarella 1597, 274c–d: "Solemus etiam dicere, in arte medica remedia inveniri ex praecognitione sanitatis et morbi. Utimur igitur nomine inventionis et fatemur illam esse demonstrationem, quae est methodus resolutiva. Nam methodum demonstrativam non admodum solemus demonstrationem inventionis nominare; etenim inventionis nomen solam respicit cognitionem an sit, methodus autem demonstrativa consistit in declaratione quamobrem sit. Illa igitur methodus ad resolutivam potius, quam ad demonstrativam videtur esse redigenda." For a more detailed treatment on Zabarella's view of the methods in medicine, see chapter 6.4.
31 Zabarella 1597, 331d–332f.

do most modern philosophers, that though Aristotle treated the two kinds of demonstrations in his *Posterior Analytics*, the division between research methods and orders of presentation derives from later times, there is no need to discuss this subject at all. As far as the question of the use of these demonstrations in Aristotle's corpus is concerned, Jonathan Barnes has claimed recently, that Aristotle did not have any research methodology as a part of science. If this interpretation is correct the demonstrations Aristotle used are really orders of presentation for a body of knowledge that already exists.[32] This was not Zabarella's own interpretation of the matter, however. According to him, Aristotle wrote about methods in the strict sense of the word.[33]

Barnes' way of interpretation can also be applied to Zabarella's own methodology. As we already saw in the second chapter, he considered that the whole of natural philosophy was already complete, at least in theory, if not in practice. This means that the function of these methods is to organize knowledge, which already exists, not to invent something that is completely unknown in the modern sense of the word. The practice of a scientist in Zabarella's scientific model is to fill up the missing pieces and correct the mistakes in a puzzle that is in general already known. Of course we discover something new when we find a piece of knowledge and put it in its already existing place; however, that cannot be compared with the research methodologies of those seventeenth century scientists, who put the structure of the universe under question.

---

32  Barnes 1975 and for a little revised version of his thesis, see Barnes 1981. See also Burnyeat 1981 and Gotthelf 1987, 167–168. For a critique of Barnes' thesis see Wians 1989.
33  According to Zabarella, in difference from Aristotle, however, Galen discussed the orders of presentation in the beginning of his *Ars medica*; see chapter 6.4.

## 4.3. Induction and the regress-method

John Buridan, one of the late medieval commentators on Aristotle's works, thought that the two main Aristotelian accounts of induction can be found in *Prior Analytics* II, 23 and in *Posterior Analytics*. He maintained that the first one, the perfect enumerative induction, is of minor practical use and that Aristotle's main doctrine of induction is the doctrine of intuitive movement from particular instances to universal principles presented in *Posterior Analytics* II, 19.[34]

Some modern Aristotle scholars, such as A.E.Taylor, W.D.Ross and K. von Fritz, have repeated the same view although they have paid attention to Aristotle's discussion of dialectical induction in the *Topics* as well. They have also noted the fact that induction may take place in different ways in different contexts.[35] Some scholars have recently attended to the fact that when Aristotle characterized the way towards the first principles as an induction, he also thought that induction may be connected with same kind of conceptual research or analysis. In that case it is a process from what is better known to us to what is better known by nature.[36]

Zabarella, however, does not use the term *inductio* as broadly as Aristotle did. When Aristotle called the way from what is better known to us to what is better known by nature, or a reasoning from effects to causes induction, Zabarella calls this process resolution. According to him, the resolutive method can further be divided into two species. One is a demonstration from an effect (*demonstratio ab effectu*) which is more efficient and has been

---

34  On Buridan's view on induction, see Kakkuri-Knuuttila and Knuuttila 1990, 294 and Thijssen 1987, 246–255. In fact, Buridan's interpretation of Aristotle's induction seems to be fairly common in the late Middle Ages and during the Renaissance. As we later shall see, Zabarella also makes the division between enumerative and intuitive induction in the same manner as Buridan did.

35  Taylor 1955, 29–40; Ross 1964, 38–41; von Fritz 1971, 623–676; Pérez–Ramos 1988, 202–204.

36  Hintikka 1980; Kakkuri–Knuuttila and Knuuttila 1990, 294–296; Knuuttila (forthcoming). For a critic of interpreting Aristotle's induction mainly as intuitive, see also Engberg-Pedersen 1979. On the role of intuition in *Posterior Analytics* II, 19, see Kahn 1981.

used to invent things that are very obscure and hidden from us. The other species of resolution is induction (*inductio*) which is a weaker type of resolution and which has been used to invent things that are not totally unknown for us and needs only little clarification. Both types of resolution are syllogistic methods whose proper end is inventing principles.[37]

According to Zabarella, a demonstration from an effect cannot be suspected. It is a syllogism leading from an effect to an unknown cause. As far as induction is concerned, Zabarella claims that Aristotle defined it as a syllogism in his *Prior Analytics*. If induction cannot be transformed into a valid syllogism, it does not have the degree of necessity which is appropriate for demonstrative reasoning. It is obvious that in this passage Zabarella speaks about so-called enumerative induction, which as a syllogistic form of inference comes close to deduction.[38] In fact, in Zabarella's view the only reason which separates perfect or necessary induction from deduction is that induction is a process from an effect to a cause whereas deduction is made in the opposite direction from a cause to an effect.[39]

The distinction between what is better known or more familiar to us and what is more familiar in itself or by nature, plays an important role in Aristotle's theory of science.[40] According to him, most principles and causes in natural philosophy are in this sense better known by nature and less familiar to us. For Zabarella,

---

37  Zabarella 1597, 268f–269a.
38  A claim has also been made, that apart from *Topics*, Aristotle did not mean enumeration of particulars, but of species. On this point, see Kakkuri-Knuuttila and Knuuttila 1990, 297–298; Hintikka 1980 and Knuuttila (forthcoming). Zabarella, however, speaks clearly about enumeration of particulars, not species.
39  N. Jardine 1976, 299, has some difficulties to understand Zabarella's concepts of induction, because he assumes in a modern way that induction can never be made in a syllogistic form. *In The Cambridge History of Renaissance Philosophy* 1988, 690–691, Jardine connects induction with the theory of cognition represented in *De rebus naturalibus*. However, he fails to see the difference between the complete induction (in *De methodis*) and the intuitive induction (in *De regressu*) Zabarella makes. As Pérez-Ramos has noted, in Averroistic logic the sharp distinction between syllogism and induction was not enforced. On this see Pérez-Ramos 1988, 231, note 35.
40  See Aristotle *Prior Analytics* 68b35–37; *Posterior Analytics* 71b33–72a5 and *Physics* 184a16–25.

however, the term "known by nature" can also be used in another meaning which is more central for him. In this sense things "known by nature" are more easily known to us because they are sensible.[41] The distinction between the two species of resolution can thus be cleared up with the latter use of things "known by nature". With induction only those principles can be recognized which are known by nature and need only minor confirmation; whereas demonstration from an effect is much more efficient. It helps to invent those principles which are imperceptible and unknown by nature. For this invention, induction is wholly useless.[42]

The distinction between things known and unknown by nature is the basis for two different kind of principles of science. Principally all our knowledge comes from the senses, and nothing can be consciously known unless it has been known beforehand through the senses. All sensible things are known by nature; not only singular beings, but also those universals whose singulars can be known by the senses. A human being is sensible and so known by nature to us even if we only sense a human being through many singular human beings rather than universally.

We do not demonstrate things known by nature through something that is better known to us, for they are obvious to us without demonstration. With induction all the sensible principles are known. In this case we do not speak about demonstration or proving, because in a way induction explains things through themselves. It is a process from something to the same thing, proceeding from what is more obvious and better known to us, to something that is less obvious to us. On the other hand, things unknown by nature are not sensible and require demonstration from a better known effect to make them evident. In Zabarella's view a good example of these is first matter (*prima materia*). It cannot be known through sense perception, so the only chance we have to know it is through generation.[43]

---

41 Zabarella 1597, 299c–300b.
42 Zabarella 1597, 269b–e. Due to Zabarella's definition of induction, it is useless in producing this type of premisses.
43 Zabarella 1597, 269f–270f.

According to Zabarella, Aristotle considered a complete knowledge to be of primary importance. He wanted to teach us the instrument, the demonstrative method, which, by imitating the order of nature, gives us perfect knowledge.[44] He dealt secondarily with human weakness and wanted to teach us another method, as well, which leads to knowledge of those things which are known by nature, but are unknown to us. By this he meant the resolutive method which leads to a knowledge of the principles. The use of the resolutive method would not be absolutely necessary, were it not for our own ignorance and weakness. Even the things that cannot be known through sense perception are not dependent on anything and could be known if human beings were not so ignorant and weak.[45]

In his short treatise on regressus-method, *De regressu*, Zabarella defines induction in a slightly different manner. Following Averroes, Zabarella first divides induction into two types. Dialectical induction is made up of contingent and changing matters, and it has no force of reasoning unless all particulars are counted on. Demonstrative induction, on the other hand, is made up of necessary matters and things which have an essential relationship with each other. Thus there is no need for counting all the particulars, because, after examining some individual cases, our mind understands the essential connection and infers the universal; that is, we understand that this must also be necessary for the remaining cases.[46] In Zabarella's view this reasoning and grasping the universal is possible, because that of which is predicated essentially (*per se*), can also be predicated of every member of that class (*de omni*).[47] As in Aristotle's *Posterior Analytics*, Zabarella's description of this demonstrative induction assumes the idea of *inductio* as an intuitive grasp which is different from deduction.

---

44  Zabarella 1597, 296e–f.
45  Zabarella 1597, 298c–300a.
46  Zabarella 1597, 485d–e.
47  Zabarella 1597, 255f: "Hoc evenire solet in illa inductione, quam Averroes vocat demonstrativam, in qua non omnia particularia sumuntur; quia dum aliqua pauca enumerare incipimus, statim apparet praedicatum illis essentiale esse. Ideo dimissa reliquorum enumerationem colligimus universale; quod enim per se praedicatur, de omni praedicatur."

For Zabarella this examination of individual cases seems to be a conceptual rather than an empirical process, even if the treatment of induction in *De regressu* and in his commentary on *Posterior Analytics* is more empirical in tone than the treatment of induction in *De methodis*.[48] In his commentary on *Posterior Analytics* he points out that all our knowledge originates from the senses. Even all mathematical conclusions come from first principles which we know by induction from sense perception. Axioms are not innate, but come by induction, even if we do not remember the exact time of this induction. Things like God or prime matter (*prima materia*), cannot directly be perceived by the senses, but knowledge of these things remains indirectly dependent on former sense perceptions. Conclusions are known by demonstration, but principles by induction. Thus conclusions are not directly known by senses, but become known through principles which are themselves dependent on sense perception.[49]

It would, however, be a mistake to assume that Zabarella always considered induction to be a self-evident process. This becomes clear if we consider the process of defining *megalopsychia*, that is magnamity or pride, in *Posterior Analytics II, 13*. According to Aristotle, we should first examine instances of men called *megalopsychos* in order to see what they, as *megalopsychoi*, have in common. We must then ask what is the common element in these results. In Aristotle's view we should continue in this way "until we come to a single account; for this will be the definition of the object."[50] For Zabarella this difficult process, could either be demonstration from a sign or induction to him. If the causes of *megalopsychia* were wholly unknown, the process would be demonstration from a sign, but in this case, where the reasons are

---

48  Lisa Jardine has made an interesting remark on Zabarella's relationship with modern notion of induction: "In particular it should be noted that it is unlikely that anything which can be identified with modern views on the inductive component of science is to be found in the writings of such an Aristotelian purist as Zabarella, who believed that the goal of scientific method is incorrigible necessary truths." Jardine 1974, 57 (note 2). Basically Jardine is right, even if Zabarella's treatment of demonstrative induction in his *De regressu* has something in common with modern notion of induction.
49  Zabarella 1597, 890b–891b,1277d–e.
50  Aristotle, *Posterior Analytics* 97b13–14. See also Kakkuri-Knuuttila and Knuuttila 1990, 297; Knuuttila (forthcoming).

3

known by nature, it is induction.[51] Zabarella believes that, by the force of induction, human intellect is capable of distinguishing the universal which is hidden in particulars. Induction or demonstration from the effect makes up the first phase of the regress-method, which was, in his opinion, the only proper method for natural sciences.

I now turn to the question, how Zabarella uses induction in his *De regressu*. He joins the two kind of methods into one process, which he calls the regress-method (*regressus*). The basis for this method is the division between two kind of demonstrations Aristotle made in his *Posterior Analytics*. As Nicholas Jardine has shown, however, in none of the classical commentators can be found any suggestion that the combination of these demonstrations had a special role in scientific inquiry. In the introduction to the first book of *Physics*, Aristotle mentions two techniques of presentation, one proceeding from the universal to the particular, the other proceeding from the particular to the universal. In Averroes' commentary on the *Physics* these two are apparently identified with the *demonstratio quia* and *propter quid* of the *Posterior Analytics*.[52] At the turn of the fourteenth century Pietro d'Abano in his influental *Conciliator* used in this context the word *regressus* to describe the relation between two procedures.

At the beginning of the sixteenth century a number of writers were willing to abandon the whole regress-method as useless in natural investigations. Agostino Nifo tried to defend regress-method against these charges and elaborated a new phase, a mental consideration, between the two demonstrations.[53] Also Zabarella

---

51  Zabarella 1597, 1199d–f,1212f–1216a.
52  N. Jardine 1976, 280–286; N. Jardine 1988, 686–688. In his commentary on Aristotle's *Physics* also Zabarella connects the mentioned passage (184a17–21) with the regressus-method, but does not consider more closely the different kind of demonstrations. Zabarella, *In libros Aristotelis Physicorum commentarii* 1602, 46: "Ideo Aristoteles manifestissime hic regressum ponit et multi sunt, qui hoc in loco eum non vident et eum audent negare." On Averroes' and other medieval commentators on the two types of demonstrations, see Serene 1982 and Sylla 1979.
53  At the beginning of the sixteenth century, besides Nifo at least Antonio Trombetta, Pietro Pomponazzi and Marcantonio Zimara discussed the possibility of *regressus*. On these discussions, see Poppi 1970, 117–137 and

tries to clear the regress-method from the accusation of being a circular proof. His main purpose is to ensure that there is a place in natural philosophy for this rationally based method which can give us firm knowledge of nature.[54]

According to Zabarella, in a circular proof B is first demonstrated from A and then, in reverse order, A is demonstrated from B. Thus the circular proof is absurd because it does not prove anything else than A, because A. On the other hand, *regressus* is a process between a cause and an effect. First an unknown cause is demonstrated from a known effect. From this known cause we then return by another demonstration to the effect. This second demonstration shows why the effect is an effect. In the circular proof both these demonstrations would be demonstration *propter quids* which is impossible. In regressus the first process is demonstration *quod,* the second *propter quid.*[55]

To illustrate the regress-method, Zabarella takes an example from the first book of Aristotle's *Physics*, where he discussed generation. Generation is known by senses, but the underlying matter of generation is unknown. Zabarella makes up a following syllogism:

> Where there is generation, there is underlying matter.
> *In a natural body there is generation.*
> So, in a natural body there is matter.

In this demonstration the minor premise is known in a confused way, because though we know about the generation and corruption of natural beings, we do not know their causes. We do not know through senses the major premise of the syllogism, but we can reach it easily by mental consideration, which is called demonstrative induction. The conclusion of this syllogism is known only in a confused way because we now know that there is matter in natural beings, but we do not know its qualities, nature or

---

Papuli 1983, 221–277. Later Nifo gave to this mental consideration a fresh thought and denied that it would be necessary in the regress-method. On this point, see N.Jardine 1988, 688–689.

54 Zabarella 1597, 479e; N. Jardine 1988, 688–693.
55 Zabarella 1597, 480f–481c.

definition. In this first step of *regressus*, therefore, the cause is demonstrated although not as a cause of this particular effect.[56]

The next step of this regress-method, however, is not the demonstration *propter quid* from the cause to the effect. We know the cause only in a confused way, and therefore it cannot immediately offer a clear knowledge of the effect. Thus there must be an intermediary step, where the knowledge of the cause must be cleared up. According to Zabarella, some writers have called this step contemplation of intellect (*negotationem intellectus*), but he himself wants to term it mental examination or mental consideration (*mentalem considerationem*) of the cause.

In Zabarella's view nobody has really explained the true nature of this mental consideration. According to him, there are two things which help us to reach a clear knowledge of the cause. In the first place, a knowledge of what is also prepares us to know why it is. If we know something of a matter, we can infer other things from it, but from something that is wholly unknown to us, we cannot infer anything. Secondly, we can compare the invented cause with the effect, not as cause and effect but as two things with some connection. In this way we can slowly learn the nature and qualities of these things and finally know that this is the cause of that effect.[57] According to Zabarella, in order to know the subject matter clearly Aristotle also used this mental consideration. We can compare our confused knowledge of the matter with the generation from which it has been born. Thus we slowly realize what place this subject matter has in generation and how we distinguish it from the functions of other principles. When we consider all these things, it is easy for us to know what kind of subject matter is the cause of generation.[58]

Zabarella summarizes the three steps of the *regressus* in a following way. First comes the demonstration *quod*, which leads us from a confused known effect to a confused known cause. The second step is mental consideration, by which we achieve a clear knowledge of the cause. In the third step, which is demonstration *potissima* or *propter quid*, we move from a clear knowledge of the

---

56  Zabarella 1597, 485b–486d. See also N. Jardine 1988, 691–692.
57  Zabarella 1597, 486e–487c.
58  Zabarella 1597, 488d–f.

cause to a clear knowledge of the effect. According to Zabarella, the first two steps can be read from the first book of Aristotle's *Physics* and the third step from the first book of his *On generation and corruption*.[59] Even if the three steps of *regressus* were not temporally different, they are at least different according to their reason and nature.[60] As distinct from circular proof, the regress-method does not end up in the same form in which it began. In a circular proof the end is the same knowledge that was the principle in the first demonstration, but in the regressus-method the end is different from the principles. It is a clear knowledge of the effect.[61]

If we compare Zabarella's treatment of *regressus* with Aristotle's treatment of the two kind of demonstrations in *Posterior Analytics* or his account of induction in *Prior Analytics*, a few interesting remarks can be made. As Zabarella himself seems to understand, the crucial point in the regress-method is the mental consideration between the two demonstrations. If we consider two coexstensive classes as candidates for an effect and a cause, how can we be sure that this is the cause and that the effect and not the other way round. According to Knuuttila, Aristotle did not have any good answer to this question, but just assumed that somehow we know it.[62] This also seems to be the case with Zabarella. He notes that no author before him has dealt profoundly with this mental consideration, where we become convinced of the relationship between the cause and the effect. His own treatment, however, appears to be just as general as the others.

In his early logical treatises Galileo Galilei also faced the problem of *regressus*. He treated the subject in his *Tractatio de demonstratione* which, according to William A. Wallace, is written in 1588 or 1589.[63] In this treatise Galileo wrote a *quaestio*

---

59  Zabarella 1597, 489c–d.
60  Zabarella 1597, 493b.
61  Zabarella 1597, 494b–496a. Antonino Poppi comes to the conclusion that Zabarella's notion of the regress–method and his concept of science are very theoretical and far away from "the pioneers of the modern science". See Poppi 1972, 290–292. Poppi's conclusions are in accordance with my reading of Zabarella's methodology.
62  Knuuttila, forthcoming.
63  Wallace 1988, 135. In this article Wallace shows clearly, how Galileo became familiar with Aristotelian science, modified by Jesuit authors working at Collegio Romano at Rome. On this point, see also Wallace 1984.

called *An detur regressus demonstrativus?* (Is demonstrative regress possible?), where he lists up the conditions that are required for the regress to occur. In one of these conditions Galileo points out that in the regress-method cause and effect must be convertible, so that one cannot be of broader scope than the other. Galileo provides the light and the sun as an example of a case where the effect is wider than the cause, and thus *regressus* becomes impossible. Respectively, respiration and having a mind is an example where the cause is wider than the effect. According to Galileo, there are many organs which can respire and still lack a mind.[64] In an Aristotelian manner Galileo seems to consider coextensiveness as an essential feature of the regress-method. Galileo, however, did not give us an explanation, any more than Aristotle or Zabarella, how it is possible to tell which one is the cause and which one the effect.

## 4.4. Sense-perception and reasoning

The chapters above raise the question, what really is the relationship between sense-perception and intellection in Zabarella's philosophy. In this respect the discussion in his commentary of the *Posterior Analytics* about the Greek word *akribestera* is crucial.[65] According to Zabarella, it has traditionally been translated into 'certain' (*certior*), but it should be translated as 'exact' (*exactior*). What is known by senses is known certainly, but maybe not exactly, because knowledge got by senses does not reveal the causes and the nature of things and is incomplete in this respect. Knowledge is called exact, however, when it is not only certain, but also complete. In Zabarella's view this exactness is

---

64  Galileo Galilei, *Tractatione de demonstratione* 1588, 113: "Quinta conditio: ut fiat in terminis convertibilibus, quia si effectus latius pateret quam causa, impediret primum progressum; unde non valet: lux est, ergo sol est; si autem causa latius pateret, impediret secundum progressum, ut patet; nam licet valeat: respirat, ergo habet animam, non tamen e contra, quia ad respirationem requiruntur multa organa, quibus possunt carere animantia."
65  On the word *akribeia* in Greek thought, see Kurz 1970.

connected with another condition of science, which is that it must be prior to nature.[66]

Even if knowledge achieved through sense perception is regarded as more primary than intellectual reasoning, it is not more certain (*akribeia*). While commenting on the last book of the *Posterior Analytics* Zabarella returns to the question of the translation of this term *akribeia*. As he has said before, the word does not only mean certainty, but also exactness. Knowledge based on sense perception can be called exquisite (*exquisita*) when it is achieved by strict observation and consideration, and is compared with less exact knowledge. But when in comparison with intellectual knowledge, where causes are also known, it is far from exquisite or complete. However sharp the senses are, you can never know a cause of a thing through sense perception. It is this which distinguishes sense perception from mind and intellect. Demonstrative knowledge is then more exact than knowledge based on sense perception and the most exact form of knowledge is that derived from first principles; which is one reason why Zabarella regards metaphysics as the best of all the sciences. In an absolute way, confused knowledge based on the senses cannot be called exquisite, but in relation to lower forms of cognition it can sometimes be called exquisite because it is more complete than these.[67]

---

66 Zabarella 1597, 981a–c: "Advertendum autem, quod dictio Graeca (*akribestera*) in Latino codice legit (*certior*), quae tamen proprie loquendo est vertenda (*exactior*) sensus quidem videtur quibusdam idem esse, attamen non est omnino idem. Nam illud, quod sensu cognoscitur, certissime cognoscitur, at non fortasse exactissime. Quia scientia, quae per sensum habetur, imperfecta est, quum sensus causas et naturam rerum non penetret. Exactam autem et exquisitam scientiam dicentes, non solam scientiae certitudinem significamus, sed etiam perfectionem. Ideo cum tali certitudine necessario coniuncta est alia scientiae conditio, quod sit prior secundum naturam. Quae namque est exactior, prior quoque secundum naturam est." On the meaning of the word *akribeia* in Paduan epistemology, see the detailed discussion in Olivieri 1983, 58–65.

67 Zabarella 1966, 1266e–1267b: "Nam et notitia per sensum acquisita potest vocari exquisita, quando cum diligente observatione et cum magna attentione, proinde cum magna certitudine, quantam dare sensus potest, acquisita sit et conferatur cum alia per sensum habita cognitione, in qua non tanta diligentia et attentio adhibita sit. At illa eadem si conferatur cum scientia intellectuali eiusdem rei per causam comparata, non dicetur amplius exquisita, vel perfecta. Quia quantavis attentio in sentiendo adhibeatur, sensus non

As we have seen Zabarella claims that he relies in his theory of cognition on sense-perception. He explicitly denies the platonist theory of reminiscence and claims that all our knowledge is based on sense-perception, even if we do not always remember the exact time of this perception.[68] In fact his whole epistemology depends on our capacity to abstract the universal from the particular *phantasmata*. For him the scientific knowledge must be certain and only in the process of intellection the necessity of knowledge can be guaranteed. This leads us to ask, whether he had a metaphysical guarantee for this conviction.

There has recently been some discussion about the relationship of Zabarella and other Paduan Aristotelians to the increasing neoplatonist tendencies at the University of Padua in the middle of the sixteenth century.[69] According to Eckhard Kessler, the real breakthrough of Neoplatonism into Renaissance psychology happened with Marcantonio Genua, who was Zabarella's teacher in philosophy. In Genua's view, the link between the material and the immaterial or spiritual was man who, thanks to his cogitative soul, was the supreme animal and at the same time, thanks to his rational soul, was the lowest of the intelligences. With his distinction between agent and possible intellect, Aristotle offered the terms for structuring this unifying process of intellection.[70]

---

cognoscit nisi quod sit; quamobrem autem sit, sola mente ac ratione discernitur. Ideo scientia demonstrativa exquisitior est, quam ea, quae per sensum habetur et inter plures scientias illa est exquisitior et perfectior, quae ex prioribus ac superoribus causis sit; exquisitissima autem omnium ea, resoluit rem in causas primas, quae a prioribus causis non pendeant. Ipsa vero priorum principiorum cognitio exquisitior est qualibet scientia demonstrativa."

68  Zabarella 1597, 641a–643c, See also ibid, 890b–c: "Horum enim notitia (ut aristoteles docet in ultimo cap. secundi libri) non est nobis naturaliter insita, ut esse videtur, sed per inductionem acquisita, tametsi temporis, quo hanc inductionem fecimus, non recordamur; a pueritia namque in singulis percipere coepimus."

69  On the rediscovery of ancient Greek commentaries on Aristotle's *De anima* and their impact on Renaissance concepts of psychology, see Park and Kessler 1988, especially pages 459–460.

70  As Kessler has pointed out, Aristotle's teaching on the intellective soul (*De anima* III, chapters 4–5) served as the starting[T] point for Renaissance discussions on the nature and functions of human soul. In chapter four he attempts do define the activity of the intellective soul through analogy to

Zabarella also used the Aristotelian theory of active and possible intellect in his psychology. The intelligible *species*, produced concurrently by the *phantasma* and the illuminating agent intellect, moved the possible intellect to cognition.[71] The material, which was gained by the *phantasma* and thus contained the universal structure only in a confused and unintelligible way, had to be illuminated by the agent intellect, so that the universal in the individual was rendered distinct and intelligible. Since this illumination was generally required for any act of knowledge, its agent could be an universal one, too, and could be identified with God Himself as the principal intelligence.[72]

Some scholars, like Harold Skulsky and Nicholas Jardine, have paid attention to the role of the agent intellect in Zabarella's methodology. Above all Skulsky has maintained that Zabarella's reliance on human reason's capacity to distinguish the universal from the particular, and his identification of the agent intellect with God, gives a metaphysical or divine basis for the whole of his natural philosophy. It is partly on this ground that Skulsky criticizes Randall's claim that the Paduan Aristotelians were forerunners of modern science.[73]

These writers have not, however, paid enough attention to the distinction between psychology and methodology Zabarella makes – nor to the distinction between natural philosophy and metaphysics. Eckhard Kessler has pointed out well that Zabarella "opposed the definition of psychology as a middle discipline between physics and metaphysics, rejected neoplatonic

---

sense–perception. According to Kessler, Aristotle thus introduces an interdependence between psychological and epistemological theories. In the fifth chapter Aristotle made a distinction between the possible and the agent intellect and refers to the active role of the soul in the process of knowing. Kessler 1988, 485. The rest of this chapter is for the most part based on Kessler's excellent article. On the life and works of Marcantonio Genua (1491–1563) see CHRP, 819 and Lohr 1977, 726–730.

71  Zabarella 1590, *Liber de speciebus intelligibilibus*.
72  Zabarella, *Liber de mente agente* 1590, cap.13: "Non potest intellectus agens esse aliud quam illud solum, quod primum intelligibile et maxime omnium intelligibile est. Ab hoc enim et a nullo alio possunt alia reddi intelligibilia. Maxime autem omnium intelligibilis Deus est; et est primum in genere intelligibilium. Ergo nihil aliud statui potest intellectus agens nisi solus Deus."
73  Skulsky 1968; Jardine N. 1976.

tendencies in interpreting Aristotle and left the question of immortality to the theologians, since Aristotle, as a natural philosopher, had not been explicit about it."[74]

There are several differences between Zabarella and the neoplatonists like Genua in the interpretation of the structure and function of the human soul in the process of cognition. Firstly, even if Zabarella identified the agent intellect with God, this was not a problem of psychology or natural philosophy, but of metaphysics.[75] Secondly, Zabarella defined the role of the possible intellect differently, seeing it also as an active faculty.[76] He called this human intellect, which he saw as both active and passive, *patibilis* instead of *possibilis*. The intellect considered all that was offered to it by the illuminated *phantasma*, contemplated whatever it wanted to, and in doing so selected and abstracted those structures it wished to know and by judgement, understood them and became itself the object of knowledge.[77] As Kessler has pointed out, in contrast to the neoplatonist writers, Zabarella saw intellection not as a process automatically determined by an exterior impulse, but rather depending essentially on human will and intention.[78] Zabarella took the metaphysical requirements of intellection for granted, but the main epistemological problem for him was how the intelligible *species* was turned into a known object. Thus the possible intellect, which worked under human volition, formed the central part of intellection.

---

74 Kessler 1988, 530.
75 Zabarella, *Liber de mente agente* 1590, cap.12: "Quoniam igitur intellectus agens est substantia separata, certum est declarationem essentiae ipsius non ad naturalem pertinere, sed ad metaphysicum. Naturalis enim considerare ipsum non potest nisi prout est agens respectu humanis intellectus."
76 Zabarella, *Liber de mente agente* 1590, cap.7: "Patibilis intellectus speciem quidem recipiendo patitur, sed eam iudicando agit ...quo fit ut intellectio dicatur actio immanens, quia fit ab ipso patibili intellectu et in ipsomet recipitur."
77 Zabarella *Liber de mente agente* 1590, cap.6: "Haec enim omnia in eo phantasmate confusa et distincta erant, sed ab agente illustrata offeruntur patibili intellectui clara atque distincta, ut ipse ea omnia intuens possit contemplari id, quod vult, tam totum confusum quam singulam quidditatem in eo emicantem et eam omissis aliis intelligere."
78 Kessler 1988, 531–532.

By defending the disciplinary autonomy of psychology, Zabarella differed from Marcantonio Genua's neoplatonism as well as from Francesco Piccolomini's idea of integrating methodology into psychology. In the case of Piccolomini, this meant the submission of method to metaphysics. Zabarella, however, attempted rathed to direct the epistemological interest from psychology to methodology.[79] This was the reason why Zabarella was so eager to discover the right methods for each discipline. For the same reason, it was possible for him to maintain that the theoretical sciences have their own means of acquiring necessary and unchanging knowledge; means which are appropriate to themselves.

---

79 Kessler 1988, 532–533. Kessler neatly sums up the importance of methodological considerations for Zabarella's concept of science: "For psychology was concerned with what was necessary and therefore always equally present in any human mind, even if unconsciously. Methodology, on the other hand, was concerned with the use man made of these natural faculties. Since this use could be true or false, better or worse, truth and error depended entirely on whether or not man used the correct method." Ibid, 533–534.

# 5. Art and nature in the aristotelian tradition

## 5.1. Aristotelian tradition: art imitates nature

The dichotomy between art and nature is typical of the classical tradition; neither of these words has a precise equivalent in modern terminology. In antiquity, creative activities in the universe were divided into two simple and universal categories.[1] Plato did not make a clear-cut distinction between these modes of being in his *Republic*, but recognizes in his *Laws* that all things which come about in the universe are the result of art (*tekhne*), nature (*physis*) or of chance (*tykhe*).[2] Aristotle had this division on his mind when he developed his own doctrine of the relationship between art and nature in the second book of the *Physics*, in the first book of the *Parts of animals* and in the seventh book of the *Metaphysics*.[3]

Aristotle drew a basic distinction between art and nature. "Nature is the principle or cause of being moved and of being at

---

1 Close 1969, 482; Tayler 1964, 38–71.
2 Plato, *Laws*, 888E. The other relevant passages in Plato are the tenth book of the *Republic* and *Sophist* 265 ff. On the interpretation of these passages see Close 1971, 163–170.
3 On the concept of *techne* in Aristotle in general, see Bartels 1965; Ebert 1976 and Isnardi Parente 1966, 97–202. On the second chapter of the *Physics*, see Charlton 1970; Ferrari 1977; Kosman 1987 and Waterlow 1982. On the *Parts of Animals*, see Balme 1972. On the *Metaphysics* Z.7–9, see Gill 1989, 120–126.

rest in that to which it belongs primarily, in virtue of itself and not accidentally."[4] Having made this formal definition in his *Physics* Aristotle drew a comparison between natural and artificial bodies. Natural bodies come into being through natural agencies; artificial bodies are produced by man.[5] Moreover, the essential difference between them is that natural bodies do something; some grow or decay, others move and manifest activities, but artificial compositions merely exist as an expression of an idea. Aristotle concludes that the difference between natural and artificial things is that natural things have within themselves an intrinsic source of movement and rest.[6]

According to Aristotle art imitates nature, which almost became a popular saying in the Middle Ages (*ars imitatur naturam*). He says that if a house were made by nature, it would be made in the same way as it is made now by art. The same is true of things made by nature: If they had been made by art, they would have been made in exactly the same way as now. Art imitates nature and, therefore, in some cases completes what nature cannot bring to an end.[7] The imitation, however, takes place on two different levels; firstly, in imitation of natural beings and, secondly, in imitation of methods. These two kinds of imitation appeared in medieval literature as the separation of the imitation of created nature (*natura naturata*) from the imitation of creating nature (*natura naturans*).[8]

There is another, more problematic commonplace, however, which has led some scholars to suppose a discrepancy between art and nature in Aristotle's philosophy. This idea was evident in the

---

4  Aristotle, *Physics* 192b21–23.
5  Aristotle, *Physics* 192b8–32.
6  Aristotle, *Physics* 192b22–23. Weisheipl 1985, 10. See also Meyer's fundamental study on the art/nature –relationship; Meyer 1919.
7  Aristotle, *Physics* 199a12–17. Tatarkiewicz assumes that Aristotle here makes a division between the utilitarian arts and the imitative arts, which correspond to the modern "fine arts". However, Aristotle himself does not make such a distinction, but such a division can be traced in certain ancient commentaries of Aristotle's *Physics* (for example Philoponus' and Simplicius'commentaries). See also Close 1971, 169,174–175. On Aristotle's use of *techne* especially in *Rhetoric* and *Poetics*, see Halliwell 1986, 46–57 and Black 1990, 21–30. On the birth of the modern notion of the fine arts as strictly separated from other forms of *tekhne*, see Kristeller 1951.
8  Bialostocki 1963, 20; Weisheipl 1985, 1.

passage of the *Physics* cited abovewhere Aristotle admits that, in some cases, art perfects the work of nature. Is it really possible for an art to create something that nature has not been able to produce? When referring to education, in his *Politics* Aristotle says that art aids and complements nature.[9] In the *Parts of Animals* he says that nature has given men hands and intelligence in order that they may develop crafts and thus overcome their natural disadvantages, such as nudity and lack of natural weapons.[10] So there are several passages where Aristotle admits that nature can be aided by human craft. These excerpts, however, do not let us conclude that there is some unavoidable discrepancy between art and nature in Aristotle's philosophy. Rather, art ought to be seen as an extension to nature's processes and products.[11]

According to Aristotle, each art has its own end; namely the good for which everything else is done. For example in medicine the end is health; in strategy, victory; and in architecture, a house.[12] Since the end is already given, it cannot be the object of deliberation. Deliberation in the arts is thus limited to means; how and by what means the proper end of some individual art is attained, and by which means most effectively.[13] An artifact consists of matter, which has a nature, but the artifact in itself lacks a nature, except the nature of the matter which it has merely by accident. Thus the artefact is an accidental thing.[14]

In the hierarchy of being, nature presents something eternal and original, while art and the product of human artefacts are bound to be something secondary and dependent on the contingent nature

---

9 Aristotle, *Politics* 1337a2.
10 Aristotle, *Parts of Animals* 687a–687b25.
11 On the metaphor of nature as a divine craftsman, see Solmsen 1963, 490–491; Mittelstrass 1988.
12 Aristotle, *Nicomachean Ethics* 1097a15–21.
13 Kakkuri–Knuuttila (forthcoming), 3–4.
14 Kosman 1987, 367–368,387–388. This corresponds to the question, whether Aristotle denied the substancehood to artefacts. In *Physics* 193a9–10 he equates "being a substance" with "having a nature". Moreover, in *Metaphysics* 1043b20–22 Aristotle explicitly states that artefacts ought not to be considered as substances, because they lack the natural form (see also *Metaphysics* 1041b29). However, *Metaphysics* 1070 a5–9 seems to be in contradiction with this view. See also Waterlow 1982, 52–55; Gill 1989, 120–126,153–164,213–222.

of the human volition.[15] Thus the concepts of art and nature are not equal in Aristotle's philosophy, because human art is generally dependent on and ancillary to nature.

> Dependent because it imitates the functions, processes and appearance of the natural world, takes its laws and principles from nature, and makes use of its material; ancillary because it often cooperates with natural processes in helping them to attain full or normal development, and more generally because it fills in the deficiencies of man's natural state and environment.[16]

To sum up, in Aristotle's works the comparisons and contrasts between the two types of creative agent – art and nature – are introduced as illustrations of the character of nature's creative processes. The definition of natural creativity is his predominant interest and the topic of art and nature are only secondary to this.[17]

---

15  Hans Blumenberg has even claimed that nothing which exists ontologically, can be enriched by the works of men: nothing essentially happens in the work of human beings. Blumenberg 1957, 273. On the concept "hierarchy of being" in the historical context, see Mahoney 1982,1983a.
16  Close 1969, 469.
17  Close 1969, 479–481; Close 1971, 170–175. For Aristotle's use of art as an analogy in different meanings, see Fiedler 1978, 168–288. It has been a common feature in this century's interpretations of the *Physics* to stress that the analogy between art and nature had no strong philosophical meaning, but played only a metaphorical or decorative role in Aristotle's writings. For example Wieland 1962, 270 writes: "Denn in der Anwendung des Telosgedankens auf die Erklärung natürlicher Dinge macht Aristoteles von der Analogie zum k·ü·nstlichen Herstellen kaum mehr Gebrauch – abgesehen höchstens von gelegentlichen Metaphern und Vergleichen, in denen die Natur als handelnde Person erscheint. Doch es ist leicht zu sehen, dass diese Stellen nur dekorative, aber keine systematische Bedeutung haben." August Mansion has stated that these analogies play a role of "pedagogic procedure". Aristotle illustrates the processes of nature with examples taken from the arts because these are more comprehensible for us than the natural processes. Mansion 1946, 229.

110

## 5.2. A Renaissance dilemma: can an art compete with nature?

The Renaissance brought the ancient distinction between art and nature again under close consideration.[18] In artistic circles the discussion aroused a lively debate about whether art should imitate nature, and whether sculpture or painting is nobler in this imitation.[19] Relevant to our present study are the commentaries on the second book of Aristotle's *Physics*, which discuss the division between art and nature.[20] The ancient Greek commentators on Aristotle clearly stated that art is inferior to nature. Simplicius referred to Porphyrios and said that nature is far better than art, but admitted that Porphyrios had considered art an competitor (*aemula*) of nature, too, when it completes what nature has not been able to bring to an end.[21] Themistius also admitted that art can produce some results that nature cannot achieve.[22]

At the beginning of the sixteenth century Paduan Aristotelians maintained the traditional view that art imitates nature. This notion was apparent already in Averroes' commentary on Aris-

---

18  On the various meanings of "nature" in the Renaissance see Mittelstrass 1988 and Nobis 1967.

19  On these discussions see Mendelsohn 1982 and Summers 1987.

20  On these Renaissance Aristotelian commentaries on the relationship between art and nature, see Schmitt 1983c, 191–216. Schmitt himself points out that a detailed study of this aspect of the commentaries has not yet been made, but he thinks that significant findings might emerge from such a study (ibid, 215).

21  Simplicius, *Commentaria in octo libros Aristotelis de Physico audito* 1566, 133: "Attamen Porphyrius inquit, hoc in loco fieri argumentum ex ipso magis et minus. Nam ars, cum sit infirmior natura, quemadmodum et simulachrum exemplari et ea, quae sunt ante finem gratia finis facit ars, igitur multo magis natura sic aget, cum sit longe melior arte. Sed quo dicit artem esse deteriorem natura, siquidem illa inquit, artem perficere, quae natura operari agereque nequit. Nisi ergo hoc ita dixerit, quia ars supplet defectui naturae, hoc autem et priorem facere potest, vel etiam tanquam aemula, imitatrixque."

22  Themistius, *Paraphrasis in Aristotelis Physices* 1549, 25r: "Prorsus perficere solet ars aliquando ea, quae natura non potest absolvere. Sunt enim quaedam, in quibus non natura, sed ars invenit extremum. Nam ad parandam sanitatem et vires recolligendas medicamenta praebentur tunc, quum natura sufficit." It is of interest that Themistius took his example from medical art, whereas Zabarella expressly considers medicine to be one of those conjectural arts, in which nature can cure patients without any help from the physicians.

totle's *Physics*, which through the numerous reprints of the so-called Giunta-edition made a major impact on Paduan Aristotelianism in the latter part of the sixteenth century.[23] In Agostino Nifo's commentary on the *Physics* the same notion of art as an imitator of nature is apparent.[24] Though Alessandro Piccolomini's vernacular commentary on the *Physics* shared the same opinion, he considered the possibility that artistic processes could be different from natural ones, and that they could even work against nature. However, he eventually denied this possibility claiming that if we consider anything artificial for long enough, for example the mechanism of a clock, we become convinced that the movement is natural.[25]

With regard to these Renaissance discussions on the nature of artistic production, Antonio Pérez-Ramos has made an interesting distinction between two kind of artefacts. Firstly there are those products of art that can be named "alchemical analogues", these are the products of something "natural" such as gold by artificial means. Secondly, there are novel technological inventions which have no "analogue" in nature, like gunpowder, compasses, printing presses and the ever-growing world of mechanical artefacts. Pérez-Ramos assumes that in the long run Aristotelians could maintain the principle that art perfects nature or imitates it only in the first group of artefacts.[26] However, as we saw above, Piccolomini included in the Aristotelian system those human artefacts which moved but had no model in nature, such as clocks.

---

23 *De physico auditu libri octo* in *Aristotelis Opera omnia cum Averrois commentariis* 1550, vol.IV, 37v. On the significance of the Giunta–edition for Renaissance Aristotelianism, see Cranz 1976 and Schmitt 1979.
24 Agostino Nifo, *Super octo Aristotelis libros de Physico audito* 1569, 206.
25 Alessandro Piccolomini, *Della filosofia naturale* 1585, 20r: "Et se bene alcuna volta accade che alcune cose artificiose sian fatte in modo, che appaian poi, che per se stesse si muovino, per la virt·ó· dell'arte et non della natura, come manifestamente veggiamo avvenir d'orologii et d'altre cosi fatte machine nellequali un movimento par che resti artificioso et non naturale, anzi spesse volte contra natura; veggendosi l'acqua et altre cose gravi salire in alto. Tuttavia, in tutte queste cosi fatte machine, se ben consideraremo l'artificio, che vi sarà dentro, vedremo, che'l primo principio che è causa di quei movimenti, sarà principio della natura." See also chapter 5.3. where Piccolomini's views on mechanics are considered.
26 Pérez–Ramos 1988, 80–81,100.

His argument that even the movement of a clock is basically natural, can be seen as a theoretical response to the alarming question of why men are capable of inventing such artefacts if man's duty is only to imitate or perfect nature, and not to create something new.[27]

Towards the end of the century the distinction between art and nature remained an essential part of the commentaries on Aristotle's *Physics*. In his commentary on *Posterior Analytics* Zabarella makes a distinction between conjectural and non-conjectural arts.[28] The passage clearly shows that Zabarella saw nature helping the conjectural arts to fulfil their functions, and not the other way round. According to him, the non-conjectural arts, like architecture or sculpture, produce results that no other art can produce, and their results are definite. The conjectural arts, like medicine or rhetoric, are only assisting factors in the production of their results, and work alongside other factors, such as nature in the art of medicine, and the state of mind in rhetoric. These conjectural arts can also fail in producing results. On the other hand, assisting factors can produce results wholly without the help of their disciplines; for example nature can cure a sick man without any help from the art of medicine.[29]

---

27 Sarah Waterlow (Broadie) 1982, 51, has discussed the question, whether this kind of self-moving artefacts were beyond Aristotle's power to conceive. Waterlow thinks that Aristotle had them in mind, for example in *Politics* 1253b33–54a1, where he speaks about shuttles that would weave and plectrums that touch the lyre without a hand to guide them. However, here Aristotle speaks about the assembly of the Gods and not human arteficers. Moreover, Aristotle himself speaks about this assembly with disbelief. Waterlow goes on (pages 51–52) to say that Aristotle might have had man–made automata in mind when he wrote *Physics* II,1 and II,8, but she does not introduce proper evidence for her claim.

28 The division originates from Aristotle's distinction between two kinds of arts in *Metaphysics* 1034a8–30. In some arts (like in medicine) the matter can move itself towards the required end (health) but in other arts (like in architecture) the human artificer is necessary in order to attain the end (a house).

29 Zabarella 1597, 1162d–1163c: "Per hoc autem significat Aristoteles artes illas, quae propter incertitudinem finis vocantur coniecturales, qualis est ars medica et ars oratoria et mercatoria et alia eiusmodi ... Ideo incertus est artifex, an finem assecuturus sit, necne, ut Medicus non solus efficit sanitatem, sed est auxiliator naturae quae magis agit quam Medicus. Orator non solus potest persuasionem facere, sed adest etiam ipsum audentium consilium."

This distinction between conjectural and non-conjectural arts was already apparent in Marcantonio Zimara's philosophy. He argued that a builder is able to make the plans and choose the materials for a house according to his free will, but a physician must act according to the laws of nature. Art is a servant of nature and, like agriculture, the art of medicine has to follow the principles made by nature. It cannot create anything absolutely new.[30] Zimara calls the art of medicine conjectural (*coniecturae*) as Zabarella does.[31]

In his commentary on Aristotle's *Physics* Zabarella unfortunately does not give a very detailed treatment of the relationship between art and nature. As we have seen, the second book of the *Physics* would have allowed a closer look at the question of how art imitates or perfects nature.[32] Even if he does not treat this subject thoroughly, however, there are some interesting passages relevant to this art-nature -relationship both in this commentary and in his collected works on natural philosophy (*De rebus naturalibus*).

Zabarella denies that the difference between art and nature is that natural things have an intrinsic source of movement in themselves, but the artificial things have not. The real difference is that natural things have this principle in themselves *per se*, but artificial things only accidentally.[33] In fact, according to Zabarella,

---

30  Zimara, *Tabulae* 1565 (*Artes sunt duobus modis*), 16v: "Artes sunt duobus modis, aut ars cuius principium extrinsecum est necessario, ut aedificatoria; aut ars in qua per accidens potest contingere quod principium sit intrinsecum, ut medicina, 2.phy. com.3." See also *Tabulae* 1565, (*Alchimiae artem possibilem esse*), 7v: "Ex quo elicitur alchimiae artem possibilem esse, quia est de artibus iuvantibus naturam ad talem transmutationem faciendam; sicut est medicina et agricoltura. Vide pro hoc diffuse, quod scripsi in speciali tractatu quem feci de differentiis naturae et artis." Zimara refers here to a separate tractate concerning the differences between arts and sciences. Unfortunately this text has not survived, even if it did exist. See Antonaci 1978, 34–35.

31  Zimara, *Tabulae* 1565 (*Ars non deliberat*), 17r.

32  One reason for this omission is perhaps that this commentary was written early in Zabarella's career. It was edited by his son and published posthumously in 1601, but it had probably been written in the 1570's because Zabarella does not refer neither to his *Opera logica* nor to his *De rebus naturalibus* in the work. It is known that Zabarella had already lectured on *Physics* in the 1560's.

33  Zabarella, *In libros Aristotelis Physicorum commentarii* 1601, 5v: "Ideo advertendum quae differentia inter naturalia et artificialia non in eo est

Aristotle did not want to make a distinction in his second book of the *Physics* betweeen art and nature, but between artificial and natural forms. However, there remained the problem that a natural form (*forma naturalia*) can also be called nature, but an artificial form (*forma artificialis*) cannot be called an art.[34] The reason for this is that the artificial form is an effect, not a cause, which is in the mind of the artificer. So an artificial form cannot produce another form by itself, but only with the help of the artificer. If the form of a bed could produce the form of another bed from another piece of wood, it could be said that there is art in this piece of wood, as we might say that there is art in the mind of an artificer.[35] A natural form is not only an effect, but also a cause. Like the form of a human being, is a cause and an effect at the same time, and thus can produce another form of a human being by itself without any exterior help. An artificial form cannot do this and it cannot be called an art, because it is not a cause, but only an effect.[36]

According to Zabarella art must imitate nature both in operation and cognition. Operation in the arts is nothing else than moving from potential to actual, which means putting form into matter like the builder lays the form of a house in stones and bricks, and a

---

constituta, quae naturalia habeant in se principium motus, non naturalia vero non habeant, imo cum omnia haec sint corpora necesse est ut omnia habeant in se principium motus. Sed differentia est ista, quod naturalia habent in seipsis principium motus per se; idest, quatenus sunt talia; non naturalia vero habent quidem principium motus in se, non tamen per se, sed per accidens, quia non quatenus talia; idest artificialia, vel casualia."

34  Zabarella 1601, 26r: "Notandum autem est, quod differentia quaedam est inter Naturam et Artem, seu formam naturalem et formam artificialem. Nam forma naturalis non solum vocatur naturalis, sed etiam vocatur natura; forma vero artificialis vocatur quidem artificialis, sed non vocatur Ars."

35  Zabarella 1601, 26r: "Ratio autem huius discriminis est, quia forma artificialis est effectus et non est causa et provenit ab arte, quae non est nisi in mente Artificis, ipsa autem non potest producere aliam similem formam artificialem. Si enim forma lecti posset producere in alio ligno aliam formam lecti, possemus dicere in eo ligno esse Artem, sicuti dicimus in mente artificis Artem esse."

36  Zabarella 1601, 26r: "Et forma naturalis non solum est effectus, sed est etiam causa. Nam forma hominis dicitur effectus respectu alterius similis, a qua ut ab agente est producta, dicitur etiam causa respectu alterius similis, quod ab ipsa potest produci et etiam respectu operationum et motuum, quae ab ea proveniunt. Forma vero artificialis, neque aliam similem potest producere, neque alterius motus est causa, ideo vocatur artificialis, non ars, quia est solum effectus, non est causa."

physician recovers a balance between the humours which is called health.[37] In the same way arts precede nature in cognition. Before an art puts matter into form, both must be known. This is where natural philosophy becomes important for arts, because it considers both of them[38] In this Zabarella follows the Aristotelian idea that arts proceed in operation, where the natural philosophy has ended up in cognition.[39] In Zabarella's view nature is both an active and a passive principle of motion, not simply active. Even if Aristotle considered it an active principle, he did not deny that it could be passive at the same time. He only wanted to exclude arts from the definition of nature, because art is only an active principle of artefacts, not a passive one.[40]

It can be concluded that Zabarella made a clear-cut distinction between art and nature in his philosophy even if he did not explicitly consider, whether arts can ever be more perfect than nature, or whether they only imitate it. The reason for this omission is obvious, however. Since the cause of movement lies not in the arts themselves, they could never be considered to rival nature. The production of artificial products is always dependent on an external artificer or producer, whereas the principle of

---

37  Zabarella 1601, 39r–40v: "Nulla enim est alia operatio Artis quam traductio rei de potentia ad actum et de imperfectione ad perfectionem, quoniam materiae formam imponit, ut de aedificatore patet, qui lapidibus et lateribus formam domus imponit, et de Medico, qui humoribus proportione carentibus proportionem et coaequalitatem tribuit, quae est sanitas ipsa et forma."

38  Zabarella 1601, 40v: "Si igitur ita procedit Ars in operatione ut ipsa Natura, sequitur quod similiter in cognitione ita esse debet de scientia naturali, ut de artibus … Quod enim in Artibus materiam et formam cognoscere debeamus, ratio huius est, quoniam operatio Artis est impositio formae in materiam propriam et ita res sunt cognoscendae ut sunt. Ita igitur etiam in scientia naturali id contingere debet, ut sicuti Artes cum formam in materiam imponunt, utramque volunt cognoscere, ita Philosophus naturalis utramque considerat, cum natura, quam Ars imitatur, in operatione ita procedat, ut materiae formam imponat."

39  For a more detailed discussion of this saying *"ubi desinit philosophus, ibi incipit medicus"* see the sixth chapter.

40  Zabarella, *De natura* (*De rebus naturalibus*) 1590, 226b–c: "Nos enim dicimus naturam esse motus principium tum activum, tum passivum; quare nihil mirum, si dicat Aristoteles naturam esse principium activum. Per hoc enim non negat esse etiam principium passivum. Ratio autem cur ibi exprimat activum, non passivum, est, quia comparat naturam cum arte, ut artem excludat et separet a definitione naturae. Ars enim non est artefactorum principium passivum, sed activum solum. Ideo ut congrua sit comparatio,

movement in nature is in the natural matter itself; for example the human seed acts in human nature as an artificer.[41] From this it is easy to conclude that if artificial forms are produced in natural matter by an external artificer, arts can never exceed nature.[42]

However, other of Zabarella's contemporaries saw the possibility that arts could exceed nature as a real possibility. Francesco Piccolomini explicitly considered in his *Universa philosophia de moribus* whether art could be more able than nature, concluding, after considerable research, that it cannot. He posed the further question whether there were any circumstances when art could be considered better than nature, and concluded that if art is considered as a human product and thus contradictory to nature, it is impossible for art to be the nobler. If art, however, is considered as an addition to nature rather than contradictory to it, then art and nature combined can be considered more perfect than nature alone.[43]

In the seventeenth-century the boundary between art and nature was blurred. Francis Bacon, for example, no longer recognized any

---

sumit Aristoteles naturam quoque ut principium motus in alio, non in eo, in quo est, nisi id contingat per accidens; naturam vero esse per se principium activum motus in eo, in quo est." Also ibid, 221f: "Patet igitur, naturam in rebus naturalibus secundum Aristotelem esse formam. Haec enim per se et quatenus est forma, est activum principium motus et eadem ut materiam determinans est principium motus passivum, quod idem significavimus, dicendo materiam ut a forma determinatam. Neque enim materia sine forma, neque forma sine materia est principium motus passivum."

41 Zabarella, *De misti generatione et interitu (De rebus naturalibus)* 1590, 540b–c: "In seminibus enim naturam inesse dicit non ut formam, sed ut artificem et in hoc differre naturam ab arte; quod in arte artifex non est insitus materiae, sed extra est, at in natura inest artifex in materia, in quam agit, sic in semine humano inest humana natura non ut forma, sed ut artifex."

42 Zabarella, *De natura (De rebus naturalibus)* 1590, 222g: "Inquit enim materiam naturalem, quae in rebus artefactis inest, non habere aptitudinem ad recipiendas formas artificiosas. Proinde dici non posse in mutatione artificiosa rem mutari, ut secundum naturam apta est mutari; quare illa non est mutatio naturalis." Also ibid, 224d–e: "In accidentibus autem hoc possumus discrimen notare, quod alia a natura et a causis naturalibus inducuntur, alia vero a nobis per liberum nostrae voluntatis arbitrium operantibus, cuiusmodi sunt omnes formae artificiosae, quae a nobis per habitum artis producuntur in materia naturali."

43 Piccolomini Francesco, *Universa philosophia de moribus* 1595, 528: "Cum apparuerit, naturam absolute praestare arti et simul solutae sint omnes adversae rationes. Considerandum tamen est, an aliqua saltem ratione ars possit dici praestare naturae. Et dicendum censeo, artem dupliciter

essential difference between natural beings and human artefacts.[44] According to Descartes, art does not anymore ape nature, nor does it "kneel in front of nature" as a popular medieval tradition asserted. The only difference is the size of these things: human made artefacts are always visible, but natural objects are often too small to be perceived by the human senses.[45]

In the citation, in the note above, Descartes refers to mechanics, the status of which in the classification of the arts and sciences was not clear in the sixteenth century. In commentaries on the pseudo-Aristotelian *Mechanical Problems* the question of the relationship between art and nature became crucial. For example, by lifting the heavy bodies could human art exceed the laws of nature; or could mechanics be considered a natural science, if it considered non-natural or violent motions?

---

considerari posse: primo dicundum vires proprias et tanquam contradistinctam a natura, ac ita obscura et imbecilla penitus est; secundo, ut naturam includens eique aliquid supperaddens et quoniam id, quod addit, perfectionem adhibet, iure hac consideratione ars praeferenda est naturae. Hae namque duae causae se vicissim amplectun≠tur, mutuoque perficiunt; ita tamen ut ars includat naturam, at non contra. Natura itaque suis viribus suaque propria conditione praestat, ars vero non suis tantum, sed cum alienis iuncta."

44  Francis Bacon wrote in *De augmentis*: "And I am the more induced to set down the History of the Arts as a species of Natural History, because an opinion has long been prevalent, that art is something different from nature, and things artificial different from things natural; whence this evil has arisen, that most writers of Natural History think they have done enough when they have given an account of animals or plants or minerals, omitting all mention of the experiments of mechanical arts. But there is likewise another and more subtle error which has crept into the human mind; namely that of considering art as merely an assistant of nature, having the power indeed to finish what nature has begun, to correct her when lapsing into error or to set her free when in bondage but by no means to change, transmute or fundamentally alter nature. And this has bred a premature despair in human enterprise. Whereas men ought on the contrary to be surely persuaded of this; that the artificial does not differ from the natural in form or essence, but only in the efficient." Cited from Rossi 1970, 138–139.

45  Descartes writes in *Principles of Philosophy*: "For I do not recognize any difference between artefacts and natural bodies except that the operations of artefacts are for the most part performed by mechanisms which are large enough to be easily perceivable by the senses – as indeed must be the case if they are to be capable of being manufactured by human beings. The effects produced in nature, by contrast, almost always depend on structures which

## 5.3. Mechanics: a mediator between art and nature

In the sixteenth century the ancient pseudo-Aristotelian *Mechanical problems* (*Mechanica* or *Problemata mechanica*), which was unknown in the Middle Ages, was assimilated into the corpus of mechanical and technological works. This text was usually attributed to Aristotle but not without reservations; however, it was probably written by Strato, a student of Aristotle in the fourth century B.C.[46]

The first chapter of *Mechanical problems* explains the purpose of the work.

> Our wonder is excited, firstly, by phenomena which occur in accordance with nature but of which we do not know the cause, and secondly by those which are produced by art despite nature for the benefit of mankind. Nature often operates contrary to human interest; for she always follows the same course without deviation, whereas human interest is always changing. When, therefore, we have to do something contrary to nature, the difficulty of it causes us perplexity and art has to be called to our aid. The kind of art which helps us in such perplexities we call Mechanical Skill.[47]

The place of mechanics, which in a way holds an intermediary position between mathematics and natural science, was also discussed by Aristotle. In the *Physics* Aristotle characterized optics, astronomy and harmonics as "the more natural of the branches of mathematics"[48], and to these three sciences he added a

---

are so minute that they completely elude our senses. Moreover, mechanics is a division or special case of physics, and all the explanations belonging to the former also belong to the latter; so it is no less natural for a clock constructed with this or that set of wheels to tell the time than it is for a tree which grew from this or that seed to produce the appropriate fruit." Cited from *The Philosophical Writings of Descartes, I (Principles of Philosophy*, part 4, 203).

46  Laird 1986, 45.
47  Pseudo–Aristotle, *Mechanics* 847a10–20, translated by E.S.Forster. For more on Aristotle's views on mechanics, see Owen 1985.
48  Aristotle, *Physics* 194a7–8.

fourth, mechanics, referring to it both in a passage in the *Metaphysics* and in the discussion of such sciences in the *Posterior Analytics*.[49] The chief characteristic of these four sciences was that they derived their demonstration from mathematical science, while their subject matter was in some sense natural or sensible.[50]

In the Middle Ages *Mechanical Problems* was unknown to the writers on mechanical matters and, in spite of the practical technical progress which is well documented by Lynn White Jr, mechanics was mostly identified as one of the lower mechanical or sellurarian arts.[51] However, in the fifteenth and especially in the sixteenth century a new wave of interest in this text arose, and numerous translations and commentaries were written.[52] One of the effects of the reintroduction of this pseudo-Aristotelian text in the sixteenth century was to elevate mechanics to the status of a theoretical, intermediate science and to apply to it the theory of subalternation, which had been developed in the Middle Ages but was still the subject of lively discussion in Renaissance times.[53]

Laird has divided the commentators on the *Mechanical problems* in the sixteenth century into four different groups. The first translators and commentators on the text were early sixteenth-century humanist philosophers. According to Laird, these writers were mainly interested in the text as a philosophical rather than a mathematical work. However, by the mid-century the text had caught the attention of the so-called "mathematical practitioners" too. The third step was the introduction of lectures on the

---

49  Aristotle, *Metaphysics* 1078a16; *Posterior analytics* 76a24–25.
50  Laird 1986, 46.
51  On technical progress during the Middle Ages, see White Jr. 1978. On the classification of mechanics in the Middle Ages, see Ovitt Jr. 1983. On the treatment of mechanical problems see Clagett 1959. On general classification of arts and sciences in antiquity and in the Middle Ages, see Weisheipl 1965,1978; Tatarkiewicz 1963 and Alessio 1965.
52  Rose and Drake 1971 is a detailed study of these different translations and commentaries.
53  On Aristotle's view on subalternation, see McKirahan Jr. 1978. W.R.Laird mentions four different characteristics by which sixteenth century mechanics was in fact distinguished from other disciplines:"First, it was a theoretical science rather than a manual art; second, it was mathematical, although its subject was natural; third, it concerned motions and effects outside of or even against nature; and fourth, it produced them for human ends." Laird 1986, 45–46.

*Mechanical Problems* in the university curriculum and this happened first at the University of Padua in the 1560s. Most notable of these professors of mathematics who lectured on the text was Galileo Galilei. Finally, the fourth group consisted of early seventeenth-century commentators.[54]

The most often used translation of *Mechanical Problems* in the sixteenth century, was that of Niccolò Leonico Tomeo, which was first published in Venice in 1525 and which spread in numerous editions throughout the sixteenth century.[55] In his commentary on the *Mechanical Problems* Leonico notes that what is done by art goes "beyond nature" (*praeter naturam*) because art must often transgress the laws of nature to effect things for the benefit of man. Mechanics, according to the Greeks, was that part of the art of building that used machines. While its subject matter is natural, since machines are made of natural materials, its mode and power of working (*modum operandique vim*) are mathematical.[56] As Laird has noted, Leonico thus accepts the main features of Aristotelian mechanics, namely that it works against nature for man's benefit and that it is partly natural and partly mathematical;

---

54  Laird 1986, 47–48. Laird has also made an interesting study on the reputation of Archimedes in the Renaissance. Firstly, Laird speaks of the reputation of Archimedes in the Middle Ages; secondly, of his "humanist" reputation as a practical artificer in the first half of the sixteenth century; and thirdly, of his reputation as a mathematician from about the mid–sixteenth century on. Archimedes was thus first considered a practical artificer and only later on a theoretical mathematician. Laird 1991, 631–638. On the reception of Archimedes in the Middle Ages see Clagett 1964.

55  Rose and Drake 1971, 79–80.

56  Leonico Tomeo, *Aristotelis Quaestiones mechanicae* in *Opuscula* 1525, f.23v–r: "Praeter naturam hoc vocat in loco ea quae arte fiunt, quomiam saepe numero ars naturae transgressa leges et nimirum efficere videtur quae usui commoditateque hominum esse debent ...Mechanicam autem aedificatorie artis eam graeci appellaverunt partem quae machinis ad conficienda opera uteretur ... Mechanicas hoc in loco quaestiones philosophus, mathematicarum naturaliumque contemplationum dixit esse communes, quam circa subiectam quidem materiam naturalem nimirum omnes fiunt. De ferreis nam (verbi causa) vectibus loquuntur et de ligneis aut aeneis orbibus, de stateris et trutinis, huiusmodique rebus quae sine controversa naturales existunt et physicam habent materiam; circa modum autem operandique vim ad mathematica declinant."

although he does not elaborate further on its scope or its relation to other arts and sciences.[57]

A more elaborate treatment of the nature of mechanics and its relationship to other arts and sciences can be found in Alessandro Piccolomini's commentary on Aristotle's *Mechanics*. Like Leonico before him, Piccolomini was a humanist with an interst in the natural works of Aristotle, too. His commentary enjoyed considerable popularity in the latter part of the sixtenth century. It was first published in Rome in 1547, reprinted in Venice in 1565, and even translated into Italian by Vannoccio Biringuccio in 1582.[58]

Using the traditional Aristotelian medieval classification of the arts and sciences, Piccolomini notes in his prologue to that commentary that mechanics as a speculative discipline under geometry aids the operative arts to fulfil their functions.[59] While mechanics is not to be identified with the sellularian arts, it nevertheless provides their causes and principles. If a mechanic wants to act as a craftsman he could design mechanical instruments and machines to do work, but as a *mechanicus* he rests content with considering their causes and principles.[60] Although mechanics imitates and aids nature, it must often work outside or against the opposition of nature in order to accomplish

---

57  Laird 1986, 49.
58  Rose and Drake 1971, 82.
59  Piccolomini Alessandro, *In Mechanicas quaestiones Aristotelis paraphrasis* 1565, 5v–r: "Mechanica igitur Scientia, cum mathematico instrumento ac medio pertractetur, nemini dubium esse debet, quin sub Geometria commodissime collocetur. Mechanicam autem Scientiam voco, ex qua causae et principia, ad quamplurimas artes sellurarias, exhauriri possunt. Quae quidem artes vulgo non recte, mechanicae nuncupatur; nam potius sellulariae, sive Banausicae ac humiles dici deberent. Eae itaque artes maximum ex mechanicis iuvamentum capiunt, cum earum auxilio complures machinae, compluraque instrumenta, domi, militiaeque excogitentur; ex qua quidem excogitatione, huiusmodi nomen fortite sunt."
60  Piccolomini 1565, 5v–r: "Licet enim mechanica instrumenta ac machinationes ipsae, ad opus aliquod excogitentur, Mechanicus tamen artifex; ea ratione qua mechanicus est, solummodo causas et principia earum considerans, in contemplatione ipsa quiescit et sistit. Ex quibus omnibus quae iam diximus, cum liquido patere possit, sub qua nam Philosophia, mechanicae scientiae collocentur."

human ends.[61] As Laird notes, mechanics is the art by which we discover machines and instruments by which in turn the sellularian arts can overcome this opposition between art and nature.[62]

Piccolomini makes a clear distinction between mathematics and natural philosophy, too, and states that although both mechanics and natural philosophy are contemplative sciences dealing with natural matter, that is with mobile and heavy things (*mobilia* and *ponderosa*), they differ in that mechanics treats this subject in a mathematical way whereas which natural philosophy does not.[63] Laird draws the clear conclusion that what is noteworthy for Piccolomini, as for most commentators on the *Mechanical Problems* including Galileo, is that mechanics concerns primarily violent motions, while natural philosophy and the science of motion derived from it primarily concern natural motions. Summed up in a few words, Piccolomini considered mechanics a contemplative and mathematical science under geometry that provides the mechanical arts with their principles and causes. It is primarily concerned with motions and effects produced against nature for the benefit of man.[64]

The University of Padua was the first, and perhaps the only, Italian university in the sixteenth century to offer lectures on mechanics. These lectures were based on the *Mechanical Problems* and significantly, the lectures were given not from the chair of

---

61  Piccolomini 1565, 7v–r: "Harum tamen rerum mirandarum, duo sunt genera. Alterum est illarum, quae secundum naturam videntur fieri, quarum, ut diximus, nescitur causa. Alterum vero, earum quae contra naturam accidunt, veluti si gravia ascendant, levia non supervolent et multa huiusmodi, quae ars ipsa conficit, naturam quandoque superans. Haec itaque, cum vi quadam contingant, praeter naturam dicuntur fieri, atque horum causam, hoc est ipsam violentiam, cum vel ignoramus, vel minorem arbitramur quam effectus appareant, miramur omnes."
62  Laird 1986, 50.
63  Piccolomini 1565, 8v: "Quae quidem, quamvis non penitus naturales, nec omnino mathematicae dici possint, sed utrorumque naturam sapiant, magis tamen mathematicis quaestionibus propinquae sunt. Cum enim in naturali materia versentur haec, veluti circa mobilia et ponderosa, ea ratione qua huiusmodi sunt (circa enim lapides, ligna et alia id genus, subiectae mechanico versantur artes) modo autem mathematico, per designationes et proportiones, demonstrentur."
64  Laird 1986, 50–51.

natural philosophy, but from the chair of mathematics. Pietro Catena was apparently the first professor of mathematics to include mechanics in his lectures, but unfortunately his lecture notes have not survived. Catena's successor, Giuseppe Moletti's lecture notes are available, however, and they provide an unrivalled view of the treatment the work received at the University of Padua in the 1580s.[65]

In his introduction Moletti, like his predecessors, asserts that mechanics falls under contemplative rather than practical philosophy, for it consists in thinking rather than in making or doing. He identifies mechanics as a contemplative, mathematical science subalternated to geometry, an account that is quite similar to Piccolomini's. The purpose of mechanics, according to Moletti, is to teach us how the difficulties of both nature and art can be overcome with a small power. As examples he lists the lifting of weights in building, the raising and pumping of water, and shipbuilding.

Moletti rejects the inclusion of mechanics among the sellularian arts and refutes the derivation of its name from the words *maechor* (*moechus*, "adulterer") or *mechor* (*moechor*, "to commit adultery"). For Moletti, sciences differ from arts both in their subjects and in their ends: the subjects of the sciences are necessary and eternal, while those of the arts are subject to our will. Moreover, the end of sciences is knowledge of causes and the truth, while the end of arts is productive work. Moletti argues that, because the principles and causes of machines are necessary and eternal and in no way subject to our will, mechanics is a science not an art.[66]

Laird notes that for Moletti the principles and causes of mechanics are almost what we should call "laws of nature". In fact Moletti asserts that nature herself makes use of mechanics, for mechanics is found in all the works of nature; although the difference between our use of mechanics and hers, he adds, is that

---

65 Laird 1986, 60. Unfortunately Moletti's lectures have survived only in a manuscript version and I have relied in the following on Laird's description of the contents of the work. On Moletti's (1531–1588) life, see Lohr 1978, 590–591; Carugo 1983 and Laird 1987.
66 Laird 1986, 60–61. Moletti Giuseppe, *In librum Mechanicorum Aristotelis expositio*, Milan, Biblioteca Ambrosiana MS S 100 sup. fols. 156–199.

nature always knows the means to achieve her ends, while we often do not know the means to achieve ours. Yet in spite of nature's use of mechanics in this way, Moletti does not suggest that mechanics is an alternative to, or even a part of, natural philosophy. Laird comes to the conclusion that for Moletti mechanics is an intermediate science legitimately using mathematical proofs yet founded on physical truths.[67] Laird has summed up some of the general trends concerning these sixteenth-century commentaries on the Aristotelian *Mechanical Problems*. What is noteworthy in these commentaries is that they did not separate the theoretical part of the discipline from its productive application.[68]

Against this background it is interesting to consider what Zabarella thought of the discipline of mechanics. As a matter of fact he was not very interested in mechanical problems, probably because he considered them to be a subordinate part of mathematics and his own chief interest laid in natural sciences. In his commentary on Aristotle's *Posterior Analytics* he, however, makes some remarks concerning the nature of mechanical knowledge. According to Zabarella there has been some disagreement about whether mechanics is subordinate to stereometry or to geometry. In his opinion the solution is simple:

---

67  Laird 1986, 61–62.
68  Laird 1986, 67–68: "In spite of its newly established status as a theoretical science, mechanics did not lose its intimate connection to the sellularian arts. Like the sellularian arts, mechanics was seen as working outside of or even against nature in order to produce effects for the benefit of man. But mechanics did not include the actual production of such effects; rather, it was thought of as providing only the principles that the sellularian arts would then apply, principles that one commentator at least (Moletti) explicitly claimed were necessary and eternal. The chief characteristic of mechanics was that it was directed towards human ends. It was defined as much by this goal as by its proper subject and methods, for the qualification "for human ends" was one of the characteristics that distinguished mechanics from natural philosophy, which was considered to be independent of human ends. The other characteristic, of course, was that mechanics was mathematical. That mechanics treated mathematically the same subject as natural philosophy was analyzed in the sixteenth century through the medieval theory of the intermediate sciences and in the seventeenth through Zabarella's version of that theory. These analyses were instrumental in making mechanics a legitimate science within the Aristotelian schema."

mechanics is subordinate to stereometry, which in its turn is subordinate to geometry.[69]

In Zabarella's view mechanics is an art which considers the means to move artificially heavy bodies from one place to another.[70] Zabarella compares mechanics with the theory of perspective and says that the subject matter of mechanics comes both from mathematics and natural philosophy, whereas its method of consideration comes solely from mathematics. Since in subalternation the latter factor is definite, mechanics is in no way subalternate to natural philosophy, but only to mathematics.[71]

In Zabarella's discussion of this there are some interesting omissions. Firstly he seems to take for granted that the *Mechanical Problems* is genuinely Aristotle's work, yet he does not discuss its originality even though it was already being questioned in the Renaissance. Secondly, and of far more interest, is that he does not discuss the problem of the nature of mechanical knowledge at all. He seems to consider it self-evident that mechanics is an art by which artificially heavy bodies are lifted. Nor does he consider the question of whether mechanics sometimes violates the laws of nature.

This seems rather odd because, as we have seen, in the major commentaries on the *Mechanical Problems*, which appeared during the few decades before Zabarella's writing, all the authors claim for mechanics the status of a science rather than an art. He must have been aware of these commentaries, especially since the University of Padua was the only Italian university where the *Mechanical Problems* was the subject of academic lectures. However, these lectures took place under the subject of mat-

---

69  Zabarella 1597, 782a.
70  Zabarella 1597, 848e–f: "Sic scientia quaestionum mechanicarum est subalternata Stereometriae, quia Stereometria absolute considerat solida, Mechanicae vero in eisdem versatur cum ponderositate sumptis. Docet enim quomodo magna pondera de loco ad locum cum artificio vehantur."
71  Zabarella 1597, 782a–b: "Nam res considerata in scientia subalternata constat quodammodo ex Mathematica et naturali, sed modus considerandi servatur pure mathematicus. Patet hoc in libello illo Questionum mechanicarum, in Aristoteles non utitur principiis naturalibus, sed geometricis ac stereo-metricis. Non sunt igitur dicendae subalternatae scientiae naturali, cum sint Mathematicae."

126

hematics, and perhaps Zabarella considered that mathematical problems were none of his business. In fact it would have been rather difficult for Zabarella to admit that mechanics is a theoretical science when, at least sometimes, it acts against nature. Moreover, while Zabarella considered that the end of science is knowledge for its own sake, mechanics was widely considered to work for the benefit of man. For Zabarella this latter quality was typical of the operative arts, not the theoretical sciences.

One more interesting detail is apparent in Zabarella's treatment of mechanics, namely the theme of subalternation. While dealing with the nature of metaphysics, as we have seen, Zabarella lays down strict rules for subalternation. According to these, subalternation is possible only in the mathematical sciences.[72] This does not make subalternation impossible in the case of mechanics because Zabarella considers it to be a mathematical discipline, but in his opinion both parts of a subalternation must be sciences. He denies the possibility of subalternation between natural philosophy and medicine, partly on this ground. If this rule is to be followed in the case of mechanics, either it ought to be a science, or it could not subalternate geometry via stereometry. Perhaps the nature of mechanical knowledge was such an irritating question for Zabarella that he did not want to deal with it more profoundly.

Zabarella's consideration of the subalternative sciences had, however, some impact on later commentators on the *Mechanical Problems*. Giovanni de Guevara (1561–1641) applied the doctrine of subalternation to mechanics in detail in his *Commentary on the Mechanical Problems*, which was printed in Rome in 1627.[73] According to him, mechanics is not subalternated to natural philosophy because they do not consider their common subject (bodies in motion) in the same way: natural philosophy treats the motion of bodies absolutely, but mechanics considers it is produced artificially. On the other hand, in Guevara's view mechanics is subalternated to geometry. Like geometry, mechanics

---

72  On this point see chapter 2.4.
73  On Guevara's (died in 1641) life and activities, see Lohr 1977, 710 and Wallace 1984, 208–216.

treats quantity abstracted from sensible matter but contracts it to the quantity of weight of heavy and light bodies, and to the quantity of the powers needed to move them.[74]

What is even more interesting for our subject is that Guevara seems to discuss the nature of mechanical discipline in a more elaborate fashion than his colleagues. In his clear division between arts and sciences there we can see traces of Zabarella's strict division between the theoretical and the practical disciplines. Guevara distinguished the use of the terms "art" and "science" that Aristotle made in the *Nicomachean Ethics* from the use of these terms at the beginning of the *Metaphysics*. Guevara states that mechanics is properly to be called an art, not a science, because it is an operative discipline dealing with artificial motions.[75] Guevara goes on claiming, however, that mechanics can also be called a science. He refers to the beginning of the *Metaphysics* and compares mechanics with medicine. These two disciplines are far more valuable than manual' arts that depend wholly on experience. In contrast to manual arts, mechanics and medicine have known causes and can be taught; both of which are qualities of a science. According to Guevara even Pappus called mechanics both a science and an art.[76] He ends with a definition of mechanics as a practical science which does not exist for its own sake, but which aims at action. In Guevara's view there are no proportions in

---

74  Laird 1986, 65–66.
75  Ioannis de Guevara, *In Aristotelis Mechanicas commentarii* 1627, 13: "Ex quibus primo dicendum erit, mechanicam facultatem vere et proprie esse artem, prout in hoc libello etin explicato textu assumitur ab Aristotele. Nam proculdubio huiusmodi facultas est habitus intellectualis vera cum ratione effectivus; qui nimirum pro ratiocinationem versatur circa factibilia, ut sunt gravia et levia, quae aliter atqua aliter se possunt habere secundum artificiosam motionem, aut quietem illis tribuendam ab eodem principio in quo est ipse habitus intellectualis ac directivus mechanicae operationis."
76  de Guevara 1627, 13: "Secundo dicendum est, eandem facultatem mechanicam vere etiam ac proprie esse ac vocari posse scientiam. Id quod implicite docet Aristoteles loco citato metaphisices, dum eodem pacto sub nomine artis, de hac facultate ac de medicina loquitur, eisque competere ait rationem scientiae et in specie Architectos (qui sane mechanici sunt) honorabiliores et doctiores esse ait iis qui manibus propter solam consuetudinem et experientiam operantur: quoniam (inquit) causas eorum quae fiunt, sciunt, et signum scientis est posse docere. Unde Pappus Mechanicam scientiam simul et artem appellat."

4

mechanics which are purely speculative; all of them have practical connections.[77]

Guevara's detailed comparison between mechanics and all the other arts and sciences is very interesting. Few of the sixteenth or early seventeenth century treatises on the nature of scientific knowledge present so profound and elaborate a consideration of the relationship between the different disciplines and their places in the hierarchy of all arts and sciences. According to Guevara, mechanics cannot be compared with the speculative sciences – mathematics, physics and metaphysics – in terms of perfectibility; however, it is more perfect than most of the practical sciences, like agriculture, architecture and navigation.[78] Having dealt with different individual disciplines, Guevara draws the conclusion that mechanics is the most noble of all practical sciences and arts. A more noble subject matter, such as that of medicine or logic, is beaten by the dignity of the purposes and the utility of mechanics, the aim of which is artificially to exceed nature itself.[79]

Guevara's *Commentary* also represents a considerable refinement of notions regarding the scope of mechanics and its relation

---

77  de Guevara 1627, 15–16: "Tertio dicendum est, mechanicam facultatem non esse scientiam speculativam, sed practicam …Practica vero scientia est, cuius finis est opus; nempe quae ex se ordinatur ad opus, vel operationem aliquam exercendam praeter ipsam scientiam. Mechanica autem facultas nullo modo abstrahere potest ab ordine quem essentialiter dicit ad motum localem, aut quietem mobilius impertiendam et ad modum quo moveri debent vel quiescere. Nam licet nonnullae propositiones mechanicae, si per se sumantur, sint speculativae, eo quod precise sistere possent in sola veritate, nihilominus propter connexionem quam habent cum aliis practicis et ordinem quem simul includunt ad praxim, vere constituunt unam scientiam totalem practicam."

78  de Guevara 1627, 30: "Ex quo triplici capite facile intelligemus, Mechanicam facultatem inferiorem gradum perfectionis obtinere inter Mathematicas disciplinas, ac scientias omnes mere speculativas secundum eam partem, qua mere speculativae, ac demonstrativae scientiae sunt, ut Physica ac Metaphysica. Perfectiorem tamen esse multis scientiis practicis, ut Agricultura, Architectura, Nautica, si modo ab illa distinguitur et aliis huiusmodi."

79  de Guevara 1627, 32: "Ingenue fatendum est nec esse artem, quae se Mechanicae arti in dignitate valeat comparari, nec esse scientiam practicam, quam ipsa ex certitudine et evidentia, qua procedit et ex dignitate, ac praesentia finis, non antecellat. Ita ut in quo superatur ex parte subiecti nobilioris a Medicina, vel Logica, compensetur, aut vincatur ex parte dignissimi finis et obiecti formalis, dum admirabili artificio intendit ipsos naturae fines Naturam emulando superare."

to natural philosophy. His *Commentary* did not consider only violent motions, as did the previous commentaries on *Mechanical Problems*. For Guevara, artificial motion was apparently any motion, natural or violent, that was arranged through machines to effect human purposes. The main feature of mechanics in Guevara's work, as in the former treatises, is that it is directed toward the production of useful work, and that it also includes an element of human intention.[80]

At the University of Padua mechanics was not, however, the only discipline where the relationship between theory and practice became controversial during the sixteenth century. The tradition of medicine at Padua held a more prominent position than mechanics, or all the mathematical disciplines together. As we shall see in the next chapter, the nature of medicine and its relationship to natural philosophy had already aroused a lively discussion in the fourteenth century – and the discussion was still in progress at the turn of the seventeenth century.

---

80  Laird 1986, 67.

# 6. The medical tradition at the University of Padua

## 6.1. From Pietro d'Abano to Leoniceno's medical humanism

Renaissance discussions of the nature of medical knowledge and its place in the hierarchy of all disciplines concentrated on two questions. Firstly, what is the nature of medical discipline: should it be considered a theoretical science or an operational art, or perhaps both of them? The second question, which depended on the interpretation of the first, asked what the relationship was between medicine and natural philosophy. Should theoretical philosophy of nature work as the foundation of medical studies, or should they be based on practical anatomical observations, for example?

The most important classical starting-point for these questions was the beginning of Galen's *Ars medica* (*Ars parva*), where he defined this discipline. According to him, medicine is knowledge (*scientia*) about what is healthy, unhealthy or neutral. In this context, Galen allowed unhealthy to be translated as sick. Galen also emphasized that he is talking about science in the widest sense of the word.[1] With regard to the question of the relationship

---

1 Galenos, *Ars medica* (*Ars parva*) in *Opera omnia* I 1821, 307: "Medicina est scientia salubrium, insalubrium et neutrorum. Nihil vero differt, si quis loco insalubrium aegrorum dixerit. Nomen quidem scientiae communiter et non proprie accipere oportet."

between natural philosophy and medicine, the essential text was a passage from Aristotle's *On the senses* (*De sensu et sensato*).

> But it behoves the natural scientist to obtain also a clear view of the first principles of health and disease, inasmuch as neither health nor disease can exist in lifeless things. Indeed we may say of most physical inquirers, and of those physicians who study their art more philosophically, that while the former complete their works with a disquisition on medicine, the latter start from a consideration of nature.[2]

According to Aristotle the speculative philosophy of nature forms a theoretical ground for practical medical studies. In the Renaissance this relationship was often illustrated with a sentence "where the philosopher ends, there the physician begins." (*ubi desinit philosophus, ibi incipit medicus*).[3] This sentence, which became a popular saying in the Renaissance, led to two opposing interpretations, however: either in favour of the theoretical philosophy of nature or in favour of practical medicine.

Pietro d'Abano, who wrote a famous treatise called *Conciliator* at the beginning of the fourteenth century, is often regarded as the founder of the medical tradition at the University of Padua. Among other topics he dealt with the relationship between natural philosophy and medicine. Pietro d'Abano's intention was to raise the scientific status of medicine and to establish its place in the academic curriculum. He did not emphasize the gap between theoretical and practical disciplines, but wanted instead to point out the unitary character of the whole discipline of medicine, and therefore called it science (*scientia*).[4] According to Pietro, natural philosophy and medicine are sister-disciplines.[5] The whole title of his main opus, *Conciliator controversiarum quae inter philosophos et medicos versantur*, shows the centrality of this topic to his philosophy. Pietro also used the slogan "where a natural

---

2 Aristotle, *On the senses* 436a17–b1. Even though very few commentaries of the whole *De sensu et sensato* were written during the sixteent century, this central passage from the beginning of the work was well-known. See Schmitt 1985, 10.
3 About the diffusion of this sentence see Schmitt 1985, 12,15.
4 Paschetto 1984, 153–181; Siraisi 1981.
5 Pietro d'Abano, *Conciliator* 1565, 9vaF: "Medicina vero est quaedam particularis naturae scientia; immo philosophian et medicina sunt sorores."

philosopher stops, there begins a physician".[6] Pietro's aim was to deny the hierarchical relationship between these disciplines,and to argue against the scholastic interpretation, which saw medicine as subalternate to the speculative philosophy of nature.[7]

Pietro's interpretations were a long time a basis for the tradition of commentaries on Galen's, Avicenna's and Averroes' medical writings. According to Per-Gunnar Ottosson, the innovation of this tradition of commentaries began to fail during the fifteenth century and the result was a repetition of old arguments without any new formulations or other progressive changes.[8] At the same time medical studies were already well established in the life of the university. The most popular aim of the students of the faculty of arts and medicine was to become qualified practising doctors. In the first two years of their studies the students became acquainted with the principles of Aristotelian logic and natural philosophy. The last three years were spent in medical studies, which were divided into theory and practice. Logic and philosophy were thus understood mainly as propaedeutic subjects for medical studies.[9] The professors of medicine were systematically paid more handsomely than their philosophical colleagues. Charles Schmitt has shown that, regardless of theoretical formulations and the actual practice of writing and teaching philosophy, socially and economically the position of the philosopher in the sixteenth-century Italian universities was beneath that of an physician.[10] It was possible that an individual could stay as a professor of philosophy throughout his academic career, but only in the sixteenth century did it become more common that the major chairs of philosophy were held by such "career" philosophers, as distinct from those on their way to the medical chairs.

The two basic disciplines of the medical students were theoretical and practical medicine. Neither of these, however, was practical in the modern clinical sense of the word, and the content of both these disciplines was basically the same. The professor of

---

6 Pietro d'Abano, *Conciliator* 1565, 7vaH: "Quare fere physicorum plurimi et medicorum qui magis physicae artem prosequunt hi quidem finiunt ad ea; quae de medicina, hi vero ad ea quae de natura incipiunt de medicina."
7 Paschetto 1984, 121–127.
8 Ottosson 1984, 124–125.
9 Schmitt 1975, 36–39.
10 Schmitt 1985, 4.

theory taught the general principles of health and sickness as well as introducing the students to the major elements of medical practice, including semeiology, hygiene and therapy. The professor of practice taught almost the same material, but applied it to particular diseases. Both disciplines were studied in a three-year cycle of lectures. The professor of theory commented, in turn, on the three principal texts: the first *fen* of the *Canon* of Avicenna, the *Aphorisms* of Hippocrate and Galen's *Ars medica* (*Ars parva*). The professor of practice lectured, in turn, on diseases from head to thorax, diseases from abdomen to toe, and diseases of the whole body, that is, fevers.[11]

This picture had changed, however, by the beginning of the sixteenth century, when interest in humanism meant that the texts of ancient Greek physicians became better known. The ultimate goal of these medical humanists was to be able to practise medicine in the manner of the ancient physicians. The founding father and major figure in this movement, Niccolò Leoniceno (1428–1524), had singled out three areas of particular concern, namely medicinal herbs, specific diseases and anatomical structures. Jerome J. Bylebyl has noted that it is not surprising therefore that his disciplines played leading roles in introducing new forms of botanical, anatomical and clinical teaching into the medical curriculum. The University of Padua became a particular centre for these reforms. Within a short period between 1535 and 1545 some fundamental changes occurred, including the transformation of anatomical teaching from a short annual event into a permanent major subject, the institution of a botanic garden under university auspices in order to teach medical botany, and the systematic use of the hospital to teach nosology and therapy.[12]

---

11  Bylebyl 1979, 338–339.
12  Bylebyl 1979, 340–346, 352–353, 358–359.

## 6.2. The nature of medical knowledge: art or science?

At the turn of the sixteenth century Pietro's definition of medicine as a science was still predominant in Paduan medical circles. At Florence during the fifteenth century the dispute had arisen, about which was the nobler, medicine or jurisprudence. Coluccio Salutati (1331–1406) had defended jurisprudence and the active life in general dooming medicine and all natural science as inferior to law.[13] Nicoletto Vernia (1420–1499) took part in this dispute at Padua, defending medicine against these accusations on several grounds.[14] At the turn of the sixteenth century the subalternation of medicine under the philosophy of nature was used to raise the status of medicine as a discipline. This approach is obvious in the writings of Vernia and Alessandro Achillini.

Firstly, Vernia argued, medicine is subalternated to the theoretical science of natural philosophy, while jurisprudence is only a practical discipline and cannot be called a science.[15] Secondly, he distinguished a lower operational part of medicine, naming it the medicative part (*medicativa*) which does not belong to the proper science of medicine.[16] Vernia was keen on distinguishing between the theoretical and operational habits in medicine and

---

13  On Salutati, see the excellent biography of Ronald Witt 1983. On the dispute between law and medicine, see Witt 1983, 331–354.

14  Eugenio Garin has edited this little treatise of Vernia, which appeared together with a treatise concerning the division of the disciplines, in the preface to Walter Burley's commentary on Aristotle's *Physics*. Unfortunately I have not been able to see Vernia's treatise on the division of the arts and sciences, because Garin edited only the latter quaestio. However, Mahoney gives an general outline of it in his article concerning the philosophical views of Nicoletto Vernia and Agostino Nifo, see Mahoney 1983b, 155–159.

15  Vernia, *Quaestio est, an medicina nobilior atque praestantior sit iure civili* 1486, 117: "Medicina est scientia nobilis, valde naturali philosophiae subalternata, quae in nobilitate iuri civili comparanda non est, cum iuris notitia, non scientia proprie dici potest, sed practica quaedam notitia nullam habens ad felicitatem munitiam viam, ut Ciceroni placuit."

16  Vernia 1486, 118: "Secundo sumitur medicina pro habitu factivo, ex medicina primo modo sumpta generato, et sic sumendo est ars et non scientia, proprie loquendo de scientia. Nam ars et scientia sunthabitus distincti, ut sexto Ethicorum ponit Aristoteles; et ista, non medicina, sed potius medicativa dici debet ... Ista est ars mechanica, qua vel consimili empyrici utuntur ... Et de ista intellexit Averroes, Colliget primo, cum dixit medicinam esse artem mechanicam auctoritate Aristotelis."

emphasizing the scientific status of medicine proper.[17] According to him medicine adopts its principles from natural philosophy, for it considers the subject matter of medicine, namely health and sickness, when it considers its own subject matter, that is, a live body. Vernia refers also to the Aristotelian principle that the consideration of medical subjects proceeds from the philosophy of nature.[18]

Alessandro Achillini (1463–1512) agreed with Vernia in defining medicine as a science, but his treatment of the subject is more complicated. At first Achillini distinguished the subject matter of the science of medicine, which is in the mind and universal, from the subject matter of the work of a physician, which is particular.[19] He goes on to consider whether medicine is a science or an art. In doing so he distinguishes two meanings of the word art. If art is not separated from science but understood as a collection of precepts aiming at a common end, then medicine is an art. If art, however, is understood strictly as a productive habit, as in the *Nicomachean Ethics,* then medicine is not an art.[20]

---

17 Vernia 1486, 118–119: "Medicina autem primo modo sumpta nullo modo ars mechanica dici potest, sed vera scientia, quae etiam subiecto differt a medicina secundo modo dicta, cum illa fundetur in intellecto practico, qui consiliativus a Philosopho sexto Ethicorum appellatur, prima vero in intellecto speculativo, sicut omnes aliae scientiae, et propterea a Philosopho scientifica appellatur."

18 Vernia 1486, 117–118: "Verum tamen est quod ut plurimum procedit a posteriori, ut etiam contingit in scientia naturali; et sic sumendo medicinam, ipsa est naturali scientiae subalternata, a qua sua accipit principia. Nam naturalis principia sanitatis et aegritudinis habet considerare, cum consideret eius subiectum quod est corpus vivum; habet etiam principia talis subiecti considerare. Illa autem quae sunt principia subiecti, sunt principia passionum eius. Et hoc est quod Philosophus inquit in libello de sensu et sensato circa principium: "plurimi medicorum, qui scilicet magis philosophice artem medicinae prosequuntur, non solum experimentis utentes, sed causas inquirentes, incipiunt medicinalem considerationem a naturalibus."

19 Achillini, *Opera omnia* (*De subiecto medicinae*) 1545, 156v: "Quantum ad secyundum articulum, primo noto differentiam inter subiectum operis medici et subiectum medicinae, quia medicina est scientia et habitus intellectus. Ideo subiectum eius est universale, quod est in anima, sed operi medici subiicitur singulare et non universale." On the life and works of Achillini see Lohr 1974, 236–238.

20 Achillini 1545, 157v: "Ex his autem concludamus alterius dubii solutionem, an scilicet medicina sit ars. Et dicamus quod capiendo artem, ut dicit collectionem plurium praeceptorum ad unum finem tendendium, sic medicina est ars; neque ars sic accepta contra distinguitur scientiae, sed quid

While discussing if Galen considered medicine to be a speculative discipline, Achillini makes an interesting division between two kinds of arts in relation to nature. Some arts just follow the principles made by nature, like medicine which only "repairs" health while nature makes it. On the other hand there are arts which make their models themselves, like painting, whereas medicine relies on anatomical knowledge (*per anatomiam certitudinaliter videt ipsum*).[21] Achillini seems to think that certain arts need not imitate nature very strictly, but for him medicine does not belong to this group. Following Galen, Achillini first considers whether medicine is a practical or a speculative science. He considers medicine to be a practical one, because a curative art is an operational discipline. He further admits medicine has both a theoretical and a practical part.[22] According to Achillini, all practical sciences are subalternated to some theoretical science, like medicine, which is subalternated to natural philosophy.[23]

As a result of the efforts of Leoniceno and other medical

---

communius est ea. Sed utendo hoc nomine ars secundum quod, eo utitur Philosophus 6. ethicorum, medicina non est ars."

21  Achillini 1545, 157v: "Dicit eam potius factorum correctivam quam factivam, ut resarcinativa, quia naturae est sanitatem facere, artis vero reparare ... Aliquando autem artifex sibi exemplum plasmat, ut pictoria, aliquando vero non; medicina de secundis est, quia per anatomiam certitudinaliter videt ipsum. Differt autem a dictis artibus, in eo quae plurima natura operante, ipsa famulatur speculationem, tam universam ex qua procedens medicus speculativus et ministrativus est." See also Zambelli 1978, 65.

22  Achillini 1545, 157v: "His autem praesuppositis resolvendo dicamus, esse practicum, vel sumitur a ratione formali subiecti et sic medicina est practica, quia arte sanabile est a nobis operabile. Alio modo sumitur ab obiecto complexo dictante de opere, scilicet sic esse faciendum vel non. Et sic medicina dividitur per practicum et speculativum, quia conclusionum medicinalium, alia dictans est de opere, alia non." See also ibid (*Quaestio de subiecto physionomiae et chiromantiae*) 153r: "Scientia practica docet constituere suum subiectum; et tunc si theologiae subiectum sit Deus inquantum Deus, theorica est theologia. Si autem theologiae subiectum sit Deus inquantum amabilis a nobis, practica esset. Similiter cum subiectum sit homo in medicina secundum quod arte sanabilis est, tunc medicina est tota practica ... Alio modo ... medicina est partim theorica et partim practica."

23  Achillini 1545 (*De physico auditu*), 66v: "Imo omnis scientia practica alicui speculativarum subalternatur et subalternate sub subalternantibus in divisione illa continentur. scientia igitur moralis naturali philosophiae subalternatur ..." Also ibid, 68v: "Ad tertium cognitio medici non est simpliciter perfecta, et quia medicina subalternatur Philosophiae ita supponit hominem causatum intellectu et materia prima, datum sibi a naturali considerandum, ut arte sanabile est."

humanists, the beginning of Galen's *Ars medica* was studied in more detail at the beginning of the sixteenth-century. Leoniceno was first to make the proposition that in his *Ars medica* Galen did not in fact speak of research methods, but of orders of presentation. This interpretation was canonized in the later sixteenth-century Paduan Galen-commentaries.[24] It was also noticed that arguments as to the theoretical status of medicine as a science were not sufficiently well founded in these earlier commentaries. In his *De tribus doctrinis ordinatis* Leoniceno had admitted that medicine does not have the certainty required of the sciences. He also pointed out that when Galen talked about science he meant only knowledge in the widest meaning of the word, that is knowledge achieved in all disciplines.[25]

In modern literature this interest of medical writers in the orders of presentation or in teaching methods has often been regarded as of secondary importance in the Renaissance writings on methods. However, this critique does not pay enough attention to the fact that the intentions of the medical commentators were different from the writers on logic or the philosophy of nature.[26] According to Daniela Mugnai Carrara, Leoniceno's underestimation of scholastic logic and his emphasis on orders of presentation resulted from the importance of pedagogical matters for him and his followers. At the same time, Leoniceno tried to break the medieval scholastic hierarchy of disciplines and raise the low status of medicine by stressing the high esteem of the discipline, which was also apparent in the Greek texts, even though Galen had not considered it a proper science.[27]

Giovanni Manardi (1462–1536) wrote a commentary on Galen's *Ars parva*, where also he treated the question of the nature of medicine. Following his teacher, Leoniceno, Manardi writes that medicine is not science in the proper meaning of the word when

---

24  Bylebyl 1979, 1985; Edwards 1976; Mugnai Carrara 1983; Wear 1973.
25  Leoniceno, *De tribus doctrinis ordinatis* 1509, XXXI: "Galenus quoque in diffinitione quae dicit medicina est scientia, scientiae nomen communius inquit audirit oportere, innuens per haec verba medicinam non esse certo et exquisitem veritatis scientiam, lato tamen vocabulo scientiam nominari." On the life and activities of Leoniceno see Lohr 1978, 538–539 and Mugnai Carrara 1979.
26  Wear 1981, 244–245; Wear 1973 emphasizes the static nature of the Paduan medical tradition.
27  Mugnai Carrara 1983, 42–46.

sciences are distinguished from artistic disciplines.[28] Initially Manardi gives an overview of the historical statements about the nature of medicine. In antiquity the topic was widely discussed and, according to Manardi, Galen considered medicine a productive discipline in many passages of his corpus. In spite of this, many recent writers have followed Avicenna's definition considering medicine both a science and finding no disagreement in this.[29] According to Manardi, however, Aristotle distinguished between the necessary sciences and contingent arts in his *Ethics* and *Posterior Analytics*. This definition is in accordance with Galen's definition that in a strict sense medicine cannot be considered a science, because the end of medicine, health, is not achieved necessarily but we can fail to produce it.[30]

In Manardi's view, Pietro d'Abano did not distinguish between arts and sciences as strictly as did Aristotle. In his *Conciliator, however,* he does differentiate between them, stating that the sciences deal with things which already exist, but the arts concern themselves with things that are to be invented. According to Manardi, this is absurd, because in that case any science ought to be an art until it is invented, and similarily every art ought to change into a science when it is invented.[31] In the same way that

28  Manardi, *In primum Artis parvae galeni librum commentaria* 1536, 38: "In qua scientiae nomen (quamadmodum ipse dicit) communiter accipere oportet, ut factivas etiam artes qualis est medicina, comprehendat. Non proprie, ut videlicet ex adverso contra artem distinctum et veris scientiis tantummodo conveniens." On the life and works of Manardi see Hill Cotton 1974, 74–75 and Premuda 1963.

29  Manardi 1536, 40: "Avicennae magna ex parte recentiorum turba consensit, putans medicinam et scientiam et artem dici posse, neque duo haec invicem pugnare, nisi utrunque pressius accipiatur. At si alterum latius, alterum pressius intelligatur, posse utraque eidem rei coaptari, sicque nihil vetare quo minus medicina ars simul et scientia dici possit."

30  Manardi 1536, 40: "Nos Galeni haerentes sententiae, posse aliquo modo dici scientiam non negamus. Proprie tamen et absolute esse artem putamus, cum sit habitus recta ratione factivus et non sit eorum quae necessario fiunt, sed finem suum, hoc est sanitatem, contingenter nanciscatur, quae arti adversus scientiam distincte sexto moralium adscribit Aristoteles."

31  Manardi 1536, 40–41: "Non enim Aponensi in hac parte standum, differentia tertia in sui Conciliatoris exponenti, Artem esse circa generationem, id est appellari artem dum invenint; scientiam circa esse, id est, ubi iam inventa sit. Ut propterea secum fateamur medicinam ab Hippocrate eam faciente, dici potius artem potuisse, quam a nobis. Consiteri enim pariter oporteret omnem scientiam esse artem dum invenitur et omnem artem scientiam dum est inventa, quod certe est valde ridiculum." Also Santorio Santorio criticizes

medicine is science only in the widest sense of the word, the demonstrations used in medicine are not demonstrations in the strict sense. If the distinction between arts and sciences would be ignored, all the minor arts (*sellurarias vilesque artes*) ought also to be called sciences, and their inferences demon-strations. Manardi, however, wants to retain to Aristotle's definition in his *Posterior Analytics*, where he defined science as necessary knowledge known only through its causes. This distinguishes sciences from the particular arts, the knowledge of which is not necessary.[32]

The attempt of Torrigiano dei Torrigiani (who died about 1350) to separate an operative, medicative part (*medicativa*) from the theoretical science of medicine, was in Manardi's view, ridiculous. He appeals again to the authority of Galen, who thought the cognitive and the operative parts of medicine were inseparabile.[33] Manardi points out that he does not consider it disparaging that medicine is classified among the arts. Citing Quintilian, he compares the nobility of artistic disciplines to the nobility of a ceasar; that is, the greatest on earth. The title of art does not disparage medicine because it also applies to disciplines of lower rank, any more than the name of a human being degrades the king even it also applies to commoners. According to Manardi, medicine ought not only to be called an art, but the most noble of all arts, as Galen said. Even if medicine is not a science in the proper

---

Pietro d'Abano on the same grounds; Santorio, *Commentaria in primam fen primi libri Canonis Avicennae*, in *Opera omnia* 1660, III, 41.

32  Manardi 1536, 42–43: "Dicam, quod sicuti ordinatio ad opus facit medicinam non esse proprie scientiam, sed solum communiter. Ita demonstrationes suas non proprie, sed communiter dici demonstrationes ... Si quis vero neget ordinationem istam ad opus auferre nomen verae scientiae et demons-trationis, is fateri cogetur, omnes sellurarias vilesque artes veras dici scientias debere et veras facere demonstrationes cum et in illis multa per causas et per effectus probent ... Et si quis adhuc resistat, quoniam ordinatio eiusmodi rationem scientiae ab Aristotele primo lib. posteriorum resolutivorum non vident auferre, quae est rem per causam cognoscere et quod illius est causa et quod non contingit aliter se habere. Respondebo, per hanc ultimam particulam artes omnes a vera scientia excludi."

33  Manardi 1536, 43: "Quare ridendus Drusianus videtur, qui medicativam a medicina sic distinguit, ut haec scientia sit, illa ars factiva. A medicina enim medici nomen, non a medicativa per denominationem deducitur. Et utroque nomine indiscrete Galenus utitur, quod ex inscriptione ipsa libri de partibus artis medicativae dicet cognoscere; in quo non minus ea, quae ad cognitionem, quam ea quae ad operationem attinent comprehenduntur."

sense of the word, it does not diminish the value of the discipline in Manardi's eyes.[34]

Not all medical writers were as eager as Achillini and Vernia to subalternate medicine under the philosophy of nature. Giovanni Manardi, for example, thought that medicine cannot be reduced to any part of natural philosophy. It is obvious that it cannot be reduced to metaphysics or mathematics, and the Aristotelian passage which Manardi cites, shows that it cannot even be reduced to natural philosophy. This does not mean, that these disciplines could not deal with the same things, such as health and sickness, which belonged to natural philosophy already in Aristotle's view.[35] While discussing Avicenna's definition of medicine, Manardi notes that a natural philosopher does not consider health a thing that ought to be produced or maintained, but as a quality of natural beings.[36] Manardi thus points out the difference between practical and theoretical interests of knowledge.

In the mid-sixteenth century Giambattista Da Monte (Montanus) (1498–1551) also dealt with the question of the nature and

---

34  Manardi 1536, 43–44: "Nec velim vitio mihi verti, quasi de medicina pessime merito, quoniam eam in artium numero repono; quo leguleii infingere nobis solent; quasi vile sit artes profiteri vocarique, quod ipsi de dignantur, magistros. Nomen enim artem adeo nobilem signat, ut imperatoria quoque dignitas, qua nulla aliquando in terris maior fuit, Quintiliano teste, artis nomine censeatur. Nec dignitatem artis nomen abrogat medicinae, quia sit vilioribus communis; sicuti nec hominis nomen regibus, quia sit illis cum plebecula commune. Alioqui de se nobile quid ars repraesentat, cum qui arte pollent, ea carentibus semper praeponant. Non solum autem artem dicimus esse medicinam, sed artium nobilissimam, quam et rhetorica maiorem libro De artis medicinalis donstitutione facit Galenus." In this passage Manardi refers to the famous dispute on the nobility of jurisprudence compared with that of medicine.

35  Manardi 1536, 41: "Non potest etiam medicina ad aliquam philosophiae partem referri. Quod enim neque ad mathematicam, neque ad divinam, satis per se evidens est. Sed quod neque ad naturalem, Aristotelis vulgata sententia constare potest, inde dicentis medicum exordium capere, ubi desinit philosophus naturalis. Quod non ita intelligendum est, ut negetur eisdem de rebus utrunque considerare, cum de sanitate et morbo inter ea quae parva naturalia vocant scripserit Aristoteles, secundoque de partibus animalium dixerit, ad naturalem philosophiam attinere aliquo modo de causis morborum pertractare."

36  Manardi 1536, 49: "Ad distinguendum a naturali, addit ea verba, ut amissa sanitas recuperetur et habita conservetur. Naturalis enim non idcirco sanitatem considerat ut faciat vel conservet, sed ut quandam naturalis corporis proprietatem."

scientific status of medicine in his commentary on *Ars parva*. He denies Avicenna's division of medicine into theoretical and practical, or operative, parts. Unlike medicine, philosophy is one genus with many subspecies. Thus it has many ends and can be divided into theoretical and practical parts. Medicine, however, has only one end, it does not have many parts, genus or species, but it is one individual discipline. Because of this it cannot be divided into theory and practice, in Da Monte's view.[37]

Referring to Aristotle's *Nicomachean Ethics* Da Monte tries to prove that in medicine there are speculations, but unlike in the theoretical sciences, these speculations are not made for the sake of speculation itself, but for the sake of practice. According to Da Monte, these are practical speculations; so medicine is a practical science.[38] He concludes that practical medicine has both a speculative part, which contemplates theorems, and a practical part, which operates on them. Speculation and action are so two different parts of the same practical discipline.[39] For Da Monte the main problem in the definitions of medicine seems to be that it ought to be divided into speculation and action and not into theory and practice.[40]

---

37 Da Monte, *In Artem parvam Galeni explanationes* 1556, 10–11: "Ergo non recte dividi potest medicina in theoricam et practicam … Quia ergo philosophia habet plures fines, sic habet plures partes. Sed medicina unum tantum habet finem; ergo plures non habebit partes, nec plures species, nec plura genera, sed est una scientia individua. Nam sicut practica non posset esset theorica, nec contra." On the life and works of Da Monte see Siraisi 1987, 194 and Wear 1973, 211–212.

38 Da Monte 1556, 14: "Unde Philosophus bene dixit in secundo ethicorum secundo et quarto quod in scientiis activis et factivis quidem speculamur, sed non speculamur speculationis gratia, sed ut operemur. Ideo speculatio ista est tota practica … A fine enim sumitur denominatio ipsacumque speculationes iste omnes ordinantur ad finem. Quia finis est practicus, erunt speculationes practicae; ergo et medicina erit scientia practica."

39 Da Monte 1556, 28: "Etenim medicinae pars, quae appellatur speculatio, est una pars, alia pars dicitur actio. Nam medicus aliud facit, dum speculatur ipsa theoremata, aliud vero dum operatur illa. Unde speculatio et actio sunt variae et diversae nostrae. Tamen est unus totus syllogismus practicus."

40 In spite of the definition of medicine as a practical science Da Monte also emphasized its speculative character. See Da Monte 1556, 28–29: "Similiter dico quod in definitione medicinae non ponitur actio. Nam medicina est scientia corporum sanorum, aegrorum et neutrorum; cum enim est actio, non est medicina aliquomodo, sed medicina speculatio est et tota medicina a principio usque ad finem dicitur speculatio. Finis vero medicinae est actio, seu praxis graecè, quia dum dividi debet in speculationem et actionem, seu in praxin et non in theoricam et practicam."

While discussing Galen's definition of medicine, Da Monte points out that the word science is used of productive disciplines only in a widest sense of the word, through analogy.[41] Da Monte admits that medicine can be considered both a speculative and a operative discipline, that is, either as a scientific habit of an intellect or as an art practicing action.[42] Following Galen, Da Monte maintains that when it is understood in the first way, that is as an intellectual scientific habit, medicine can be called science, but practiced in the second way it is better termed an art.[43]

Da Monte agrees with Aristotle that the knowledge of causes is more difficult than the knowledge of perceptive particulars. When medicine is regarded as a scientific habit, study of it begins with the consideration of causes, but when we want to teach the subject we have to begin with the things that are more familiar to us. Because we know health and its signs, therefore, we must begin with the body and proceed to the causes.[44] For Da Monte the latter

---

41  Da Monte 1556, 119: "Aliae autem scientiae non dicuntur propriae, sed factivae. Unde hoc nomen scientia usurpatur etiam per analogiam et per similitudinem in scientiis factivis."

42  Da Monte 1556, 121: "Itaque medicina est scientia, estque ars, et scientia medicina respectu diversorum. Erit enim scientia, si comparabitur ad habitum scientificum, qui non exercet artem; tamen eam potest exercere, quando habetur talis habitus scientificus dicitur scientia factiva, quia comparatur ad talem habitum ... Si autem comparetur ad artificium extrinsecus, tunc medicina erit ars, non scientia. Quod artificium separatur ab habitu scientiae, quemadmodum est de artificio empiricorum."

43  Da Monte 1556, 136: "Nam Galenos proponit unum, quod medicina potest dupliciter considerari. Uno modo prout est habitus scientificus ipsius intellectus; alio modo, ut est artificium, per quod exercet operationem. Si primo modo capitur, tunc dicitur et est scientia, quia versatur circa causas et principia, circa signa et circa corpora, ita est habitus scientificus intellectus. Sed sumpta secundo modo, prout est artificium exterius sine ullo dubio potius debet dici ars, quam scientia." As Nancy Siraisi has noted, also in his commentary on Avicenna's *Canon* Da Monte considers medicine both an art and a science. Siraisi 1987, 100–101, 229–231.

44  Da Monte 1556, 139: "Nam aliter se habet ista ars, ut est habitus scientificus et aliud est, ut est operatio. Et quoniam, ut dicit Aristo. in proemio physicorum innata est nobis via a notioribus, sed notiora sunt ipsa particularia et individa, cognoscuntur per sensum et cognitio causarum difficilior est, quia cognoscitur per intellectum. Propterea Gale. bene meminit duplicem habitudinem medicinae seu scientiae. Et ideo una est habitudo scientiae per habitum scientificum et tunc incipimus considerare a causis, tanquam a prioribus. Sed quando volumus docere artem, tunc incipimus a notioribus nobis ad faciliorem doctrinam, quoniam prius cognoscere debemus signa sana et in sanitate. Ergo primum debes incipere a corpore, deinde a signis, tum causis."

experience is nothing else than remembering many particulars, which go to form an universal theorem and further an art from these theorems. An art is then only a collection of many theorems having a similar end.[45] This definition is reminiscent of the first book of Aristotle's *Metaphysics*, where he traces the different kinds of human cognition from the memory of sense experiences into an art.[46]

Da Monte also refers to the aforementioned Aristotelian passage from *On the senses* (*De sensu et sensato*), but his conclusions differ from Manardi's. According to Da Monte, this text of Aristotle shows that medicine is a subalternative science to natural philosophy, and can be considered as some kind of extension to it. A human body can also be the subject matter of natural philosophy as well as of medicine, but only medicine aims at recovering it.[47] In the order of presentation of natural sciences, the human body is the last step. When we add something to this and begin to talk about a sick body which ought to be cured, we have stepped into another, subalternative discipline, namely medicine. In Da Monte's view the end of medicine is health and a physician considers everything in respect to it.[48] As Aristotle showed in his *De generatione animalium*, when the qualities of the human body are considered without reference to sickness or health, we are in

---

45  Da Monte 1556, 164–165: "Experientia autem nihil aliud est, nisi memoria multorum particularium, quibus habitis postea fit universale theorema; ex quo theoremate post nascitur ars. Nam nihil aliud est ars, nisi collectio multorum theorematum habentium aliquem finem communem."

46  On this subject, see chapter 2.1.

47  Da Monte 1556, 12–13: "Quod idem assignat Aristoteles in libro de sensu et sensato, inquiens, ubi desinit Philosophus, qui desinit a speciebus animalibus, incipit medicus determinans a forma etiam rationem. Unde dico quod medicina subalternatur philosophiae naturali per additamentum, eo quia additur corpori humano ipsa sanitas a medico. Quod corpus ut corpus humanum tantum erat substantia in philosophia, sed medicus habet considerare corpus humanum sanabile, quatenus sanabile est." Also ibid, 45: "Quia Aristoteles in libro de sensu et sensato dicit, habitis omnibus rationibus corpori humani tunc philosophus cessat et ibi ad eam sequitur alia scientia subalterna, quae est medicina. Ubi enim desinit philosophus, ibi incipit elegans medicus."

48  Da Monte 1556, 46: "Nam corpus humanum est sumptum pro ultimo in philosophia naturali. Si vero corpori humano addatur aliud et dicatur corpus humanum sanabile, vel aegrotabile, fit alia scientia subalternata, quae est medicina. Unde dico, quod sanitas est finis medicinae, quia omnia considerat medicus in medicina propter sanitatem et est tota practica, quia omnia in ea considerata sunt propter sanitatem, gratia cuius movetur medicus."

the realm of the natural philosopher. When we add the consideration of health to this, as Galen did, we are in medicine. The end which makes a physician operate, is health.[49]

Oddo degli Oddi (1478–1558) was closer to Manardi than to Da Monte regarding this question of the relationship between natural philosophy and medicine. Degli Oddi thought that in a proper sense medicine is a productive discipline and can be called an art but as Galen pointed out, a specific theoretical part with a particular end can be distinguished from the rest of the discipline.[50] However, in contrast to the philosophy of nature, medicine is a science only in the wider meaning of the word. In addition the natural philosopher deals with health and sickness as they appear in the nature, when a physician tries to restore the health and remove the sickness. Oddo degli Oddi follows Aristotle in stating that it is appropriate for the artistic disciplines to consider things that are under human volition.[51]

Of the medical professors at the University of Padua in the sixteenth century Bernardino Paterno offered most severe critique against natural philosophy as a basis of the art of medicine.[52]

---

49 Da Monte 1556, 47: "Dico quandoque consideratio fit de corpore humano sine sanitate, nec consideramus, quae sunt in corpore humano ad sanitatem spectantia ut temperaturas et similia non pro sanitate, sed quae sint et quomodo, ut facit Aristoteles in libris de generatione animalium; haec consideratio, vel speculatio pertinet ad philosophum naturalem, et non ad medicum. Sed quandocunque consideratur corpus humanum et quae sunt in corpore humano, ut temperaturae, referendo omnia ad sanitatem, ut facit Galenus, propter quem finem movetur artifex considerans omnia ratione illius finis, tunc illa consideratio spectat ad medicum. Propterea quod talis consideratio tota refertur ad sanitatem, quae sanitas est finis intentus, qui movet medicum ad operandum."

50 Oddi de Oddis, *In librum Artis medicinalis Galeni* 1574, 26: "Ex quo etiam clarissime constat totam medicinam esse practicam ratione finis communis, a quo totius artis nomen desumitur, tametsi pars theorica a fine particulari ab alia medicinae parte distincto dici possit, de quibus quidem finibus particularibus a Galeno diffusius habetur disceptatio. At si proprie loquamur, medicina neque theorica, neque practica dici promeretur, sed factiva." On the life of Oddi see Siraisi 1987, 192–193.

51 De Oddi 1574, 23: "Medicina igitur a naturali distinguitur, tum quia est scientia communiter, tum quia naturalis considerat prima initia sanitatis et aegritudinis, ut a natura tantum sunt, medicus autem ut ad opus referuntur ut scilicet sanitas est conservabilis, vel amissa recuperabilis, siquidem artificis opus est considerare quae a voluntate proveniunt, ut Aristoteles testatur."

52 Bernardino Paterno was the first ordinary professor of theoretical medicine at Padua between 1563 and 1592; that is when Zabarella taught philosophy of nature at the same university. On Paterno, see Siraisi 1987, 106–107, 110–111.

A medical writer should not consider such topics as time, place, plurality of worlds, the eternity of the world, the existence of a void, the nature of matter, the movement or stability of the earth, the laws of motion or any other things philosophers dispute about. Paterno even claimed that these subjects were useless for the whole human race; discussion of them being irrelevant not only to medicine, but also to morals and civil virtue.[53] Medical writers who wanted to ornament their texts with philosophical authors and arguments were gravely at fault in Paterno's view, because the nothing should be added to medical texts that did not contribute to the purpose of finding the best way to proceed in medical treatment.[54]

As we have seen, opinions concerning the nature of medicine and its relationship to natural philosophy varied quite considerably among the medical writers at the University of Padua during the sixteenth century. These commentators were unanimous about the end of medical discipline, but the opinions of its place in the hierarchy of disciplines varied a lot. However, in order to raise the status of the art of medicine two main strategies were adopted. First, the value of artistic disciplines, as opposed to the theoretical sciences, was emphasized, as is found in Manardi. In this strategy, medicine was considered the crown of all arts, and it was no shame to call it an art. In the second place, medicine could be regarded as a subalternative extension of theoretical natural

---

53  Paterno *Explanationes in primam fen primi Canonis Avicennae* 1596, 1r: "Verum non omnia quae a philosophis tractantur a medico inquirenda esse voluit, cum ex his quaedam inutilia esse non solum morali et civili virtuti, verum et arti medicae censuerit, atque etiam toti humano generi, veluti quae de tempore, loco, et de mundo, at unus sit vel plures, genitus vel aeternus, an extra ipsum vacuum, et alia, quae a philosophis disputari solent, ut scilicet, an omnia sint unum vel multa, an omnia moveantur, vel quiescant, an omnia generentur, et corrumpantur, et id genus alia. Quae Socrates apud Xenophontem tanquam humano generi omnino inutilia despexit."

54  Paterno 1596, f.9v: "Nisi forte putavit Averroes, cum Aristotelis philosophica, quaedam surripi a medicis elegantibus, ad ornatum quae vere medicinae non sint, quod tamen neque Galeno neque bonis medicis placet, cum a scientia naturali nihil a medico surreptum sit ad ornatum, sed omnia ad rectam operandi rationem inveniendam sumpserit." As Nancy Siraisi has noted, in practice, however, it was very hard for Paterno to live up his own recommendation. In his commentary Paterno "devoted a number of pages to such topics as the forms of the elements and the difference between Platonic and Aristotelian concepts of soul." Siraisi 1987, 235.

philosophy, as in Da Monte. In this way medicine came closer to the more noble theoretical sciences.[55]

In spite of these different views regarding the nature of medicine, it was, a common intention among all these writers to raise the status of medicine in the hierarchy of disciplines. In addition, Manardi represented the idea of medical progress is in embryo. As opposed to the Aristotelian view, he thought that there was much more to be researched when compared with the things that were already known. One of the greatest hindrance to the development of medicine was, he felt, the reliance on past authorities. Modern writers were unwilling to add anything to these earlier claims.[56]

Perhaps Manardi would not have been as pessimistic about the progress in medical disciplines had he lived half a century later. In the years following Manardi's death considerable progress was achieved at least in one branch of medical studies, namely anatomy. Perhaps the progress in anatomy led Santorio Santorio to remark at the beginning of the seventeenth century that in his days in medical faculties were invented many useful instruments which were unknown in the times of Hippocrates and Galen.[57] Of course all reliance on past authorities was not immediately cast away, but in the works of sixteenth-century writers on anatomy, a firm basis was laid for a new, experimental discipline.

---

55  As we have seen, Da Monte denied the division of the discipline into theory and practice and emphasized instead the rational basis of the whole medicine. See also Da Monte 1556, 46: "Itaque dixit ibi incipit medicus, ubi desinit philosophus. Et bene dixit elegans propter medicos empiricos, qui non debent dici elegantes, qui non procedent ratione, sed experientia et observationibus; dogmatici autem sunt veri medici et elegantes." In this passage Da Monte refers to the classical division between medical "empirists" and "rationalists". For an excellent overview of this division in antiquity, see Frede 1990.

56  Manardi 1536, 36: "Sed illius potius tenendum, esse longe plura, quae nondum vestigari potuerunt, quam ea quae humano ingenio sunt adinventa. Ut adhuc verumsit illud Aristotelicum, maximam eorum quae scimus partem, minimam esse eorum quae ignoramus. Quare cum adhuc in omnibus scientiis plurima supersint investiganda, hoc unum longo tempore peccaverunt maiores nostri, quod inventis stantes, oraculique loco habentes quaecunque a senioribus scripta erant, nihil artibus adiecerunt. Quod potissimum in medicina magna cum iactura hactenus peccatum est."

57  Santorio *Commentaria in primam fen primi libri Canonis Avicennae* in *Opera omnia III* 1660, 9a: "Multa quoque inveniuntur in medica facultate his temporibus, quae fortasse tempore Hippocrate et Galeni non erant. Nos diu insudavimus et invenimus nonnulla instrumenta medicinae utilia."

## 6.3. Anatomy as a basis of medical science

As we saw above, among the commentators on the theory of medicine there was some attempt made to base medicine on observational knowledge acquired through the senses. This tendency was éven more obvious among writers on anatomy. In classical antiquity Galen had already listed various uses of anatomical knowledge.

> Anatomical knowledge has one application for the man of science who loves knowledge for its own sake, another for him who values it only to demonstrate that Nature does nothing in vain, a third for one who provides himself from anatomy with data for investigating a function, physical or mental, and yet another for the practioner who has to remove splinters and missiles efficiently, to excise parts properly, or to treat ulcers, fistulae and abscesses. Now all this (last application of anatomy) is most necessary, and a really good physician must first of all have practice in it, and next in the actions of the inner organs, which are important for diagnosing diseases. For some functions are of greater moment to natural philosophers than to physicians, both for pure knowledge and to show how the artifice of Nature is perfectly worked out in every part.[58]

In the Middle Ages and Renaissance anatomy was not considered a separate discipline but as one of the practical parts of medical art. At the beginning of the fourteenth century some human dissections were performed and Mondino de Liuzzi (d.1326) wrote a textbook on anatomy, which became the standard work in the field until the sixteenth century. In the late fifteenth and early sixteenth centuries the development in humanism had implica-

---

58 Galen, *On anatomical procedures* (ed. by Charles Singer) 1959, 33–34. In this passage Galen uses one famous saying about nature, namely that "nature does nothing in vain". Aristotle also uses this expression (*Parts of Animals* 658a9). R. J. Hankinson 1989, 214, thinks, however, in contrast to Aristotle's purely metaphorical use of this phrase, Galen considers it strictly and literary true that Nature does nothing in vain. Moreover, for Galen nature also arranges things in the best possible way. For a different interpretation of Aristotle's teleology, see Boylan 1984. In his interpretation of this passage from the beginning of *On Anatomical Procedures,* Hankinson also states that Galen thinks it is just the ignorance of anatomy that allows some theorists to overlook the teleological structure of nature (ibid, 224).

tions for medical art as well. The original Greek medical texts were rediscovered, and Galen became the first and most powerful author on medical matters. Medieval Arab authorities came under attack in matters of medicine from leading medical humanists. Galen's own dissection manual *On anatomical procedures* was translated into Latin in 1531 for the first time, and this had a further impact on the growth of anatomical studies in Italian universities.[59] This translation was not, however, the starting point of Renaissance anatomical writings. At the end of the previous century new manuals for the anatomical art had been written by trained anatomists from Bologna and Padua, which had become the leading universities in medical studies. What is noteworthy in these texts with regard to this study, is that they claimed a new scientific status for anatomy.

In 1502 two entirely different anatomical treatises were published. Gabriele de Zerbi (1445–1505), the author of first of these, was a teacher of the theory of medicine at Padua.[60] He wrote his *Liber anathomie corporis humani* in his late fifties and declaring that his purpose was to show that the principal authorities do not disagree in anatomical matters. The other writer, Alessandro Benedetti (c.1450–1512) was also a teacher at Padua from 1490 onwards, where he taught practical medicine and anatomy.[61] What makes his *Anatomice, sive de Hystoria corporis humani* quite different from Zerbi's and Mondino's is that he relies exclusively on Greek authors. Thus he belongs to the group of early sixteenth century medical writers which R.K.French has called the "Hellenists".[62]

In spite of the differences in the authorities used by Zerbi and

---

59  Siraisi 1990, 190–191.
60  On the life of Zerbi, see Lind 1975, 141–146.
61  On the life of Benedetti, see Lind 1975, 69–72. On the intentions of Zerbi and Benedetti, see also Premuda 1983, 422–427. There has been some dispute on the actual publishing date of Benedetti's *Anatomice*, but the year 1502 seems most probable (the preface is dated already on 1497). On this point see Lind 1975, 76–77.
62  French 1985, 47. There seems to be a slight discrepancy in the use of terms such as scholasticism, humanism and hellenism with regard to the medical authors of the sixteenth century. R. K. French maintains that the words scholasticism and humanism do not tell us anything about the nature of these writers (ibid, 48). Instead of these terms he prefers the word hellenism, which refers to all the medical – and other – authors who relied solely on ancient

Benedetti, they have one common aim: to raise the status of anatomy as an independent and useful discipline and the basis of medical studies.[63] This becomes clear from the prefaces to their works. Benedetti dedicates his work on anatomy to emperor Maximilian I and says that anatomy is a part of philosophy and related to medicine. Indeed, he states that the entire theory and practice of medicine and the discipline of surgery depend on anatomy.[64] Gabriele de Zerbi refers even more straightforwardly to the fact that anatomy is like the alphabets of medicine and should be studied as the principal basis of medical art.[65] He also had a clear idea of anatomy based on sense perception, not on intellectual reasoning. He felt that the manual operation directed by the senses of sight and touch would lead to knowledge without much reasoning, because singular things are nearest the senses and therefore easiest for us to know.[66] Zerbi was also eager to deny the accusations that anatomy was a pure manual art. According to him it is subalternated to natural philosophy and medicine, but is not part of them. Anatomy is not just an operational faculty, but also has a theoretical part, as in defining the number of the limbs of the human body.[67]

Perhaps the most eminent of all early sixteenth century ana-

---

Greek sources. In part of the research literature the early sixteenth century movement in medicine has been characterized as "medical humanism", which is undoubtly a more general term. See Bylebyl 1979, Edwards 1976.

63  The third often mentioned anatomical study from the beginning of the sixteenth century, Alexander Achillini's anatomical studies (*De humani corporis anatomia*), was published posthumously at Bologna in 1520 and again in Padua at 1521, but this work does not deal with the nature of anatomy as a discipline. Instead, as we saw in the previous chapter, Achillini relies on anatomy as a basis for medical knowledge.

64  Benedetti, *Anatomice* 1528, f. 6v–r: "Medendi quoque ratio omnis, ususque, ac chirurgica disciplina hic pendet ... Hanc philosophiae partem, quam medicinae ars ex disciplinae confinio in sese familiarius recepit."

65  Zerbi *Liber anathomie corporis humani* 1502, f. 3r: "Tanta itaque est doctrine huius evidentia ut multitudis usus anathomiam dicat esse alphabetum medicorum in qua propriis instruendi sunt accidentes ad artes medicine. Sicut litteras alphabeti prius vocetur debens discere et legere et est sermo iste Gentilis." Zerbi refers here to Gentile da Foligno's work.

66  Zerbi 1502, 3r: "Evidentissimus propterea est modus anathomiam tradendi; cum ipse sit obiecti presentis in eo quod praesens est notitia intuitiva per manualem operationem visu et tactu comprehensam absque multa ratiocinio. Sunt nam singularia notiora nobis, quia sensui propinquiora."

67  Zerbi 1502, 3r: "Subalternatur scientia anathomie philosophiae naturali sicuti et tota medicina. Licet non sit pars scientie naturalis, quae quam non

tomists was Berengario da Carpi (1470–1530), who taught surgery at the University of Bologna between 1502 and 1526.[68] In 1521 Carpi wrote a commentary on Mondino's work, his aim, according to French, being to found a new way of writing about anatomy based on sense perception (*anatomia sensibilis*). He was also unique among his predecessors and contemporaries in producing a dissection-based anatomy in commentary form.[69] At the beginning of his *Commentaria super anatomia Mundini* Carpi states that anatomy is necessary not only for physicians but also for philosophers. Anatomy can reveal the secrets of nature and show the power of the Creator.[70] In medicine a physician cannot know the sicknesses of the internal organs without it. Moreover, it is also necessary for curing sickness and in maintaining the health of the human body. Lastly, physicians have to rely on anatomical knowledge in making prognoses, too.[71] Like Zerbi Carpi cites Gentile da Foligno's argument as to anatomy's usefulness and its place as the foundation for all medical learning.[72]

---

immediate vocet modum et qualitatem operandi: est doctrina theorica. Iam nam notum est quae cognitio rerum quae a medicis dicunt naturales de quoque numero sunt membra corporis humani, circa que anathomicus versatur: est theorica." Loris Premuda sees in the works of Benedetti and Zerbi the seeds of modern anatomical and medical research. Premuda 1983, 423–426.

68 On Carpi's life see French 1985, 43–49. L. R. Lind has called these early sixteenth century anatomists "pre-Vesalians", because for him Vesalius was a genius and the turning-point of the whole art of anatomy. French (ibid, 42) has criticized Lind's attitude in the following words: "In particular historians have attempted to group together the people who wrote anatomies before 1543 as "pre-Vesalians". The implication is not merely that they were earlier than Vesalius, but that they were not so good as Vesalius. Thus Lind speaks of the reasons (too much philosophy and not enough dissection) for their "failure" (that is, their failure to be Vesalius). But the preVesalians were not striving towards a common goal, nor attempting to hit upon the proper method of proceeding."

69 French 1985.

70 Carpi, *Commentaria super anatomia Mundini* 1521, 5v: "Utilitas Anatomiae et necessitas non solum requiritur sciri a Medico, verum etiam a Philosopho rimanti secreta naturae, ubi valde per anatomiam admirantur de potentia creatoris."

71 Carpi 1521, 5r: "Et quod sit necessaria anatomia Medico, clarum est quia non possunt cognosci aegritudines membrorum interiorum absque ea ... Igitur anatomia est necessaria et non solum in cognoscendis aegritudinibus, verum etiam in curandis et etiam in praeservandis et conservandis corporibus in sanitate ... Et iuvat non solum anatomia in cura perficiendia, verum etiam in prognosticum."

72 Carpi 1521, 5r: "Tanta est igitur anatomiae necessitas et utilitas, ut multitudinis usus dicet eam esse Alphabetum Medicorum, in qua prius instruendi

And thus a physician who ignores anatomy is like the blind leading the blind; both are falling into a pit, of which, these days, we see numerous examples.[73]

Having demonstrated the usefulness and necessity of anatomical knowledge, Carpi turns to the definition and nature of this discipline. In his view there are two ways to define anatomy. First it can be understood as a clarification of all the things that are hidden in the human body. In this sense anatomy is not theoretical or practical, but a manual operation. Medicine is a science (*scientia*) whose end is health, and anatomy can be understood as an instrument of medical science, not as a science itself.[74]

Secondly, anatomy can be defined as a science (*scientia*). This definition can itself be understood in two ways. Firstly, anatomy is a science that knows the simple and composite parts of human body, their place, operations and so on. Understood this way anatomy become part of theoretical medicine, helping theoretical medicine and natural philosophy.[75] Secondly it can be defined as scientific knowledge of the parts of the human body, which also covers the manual operation and demonstration of these parts. When anatomical knowledge helps us to know the parts of human body and the reasons for illnesses, it is part of theoretical medicine, but when it helps to cure illnesses, it is a part of practical medicine. Carpi points out that in discussing these

---

sunt accedentes ad medicinam, sicut litteras Alphabeti prius docentur, debentes legere et discere per eas haec Gentilis."

73  Carpi 1521, 5r: "Et ita Medicus qui ignorat anatomiam est tanquam caecus caecum ducens et ambo in foveam cadunt, ut in dies per diversa videmus exempla."

74  Carpi 1521, 6v: "Noto primo quae anatomia capit dupliciter. Uno modo prout est artificiosa actualis incisio et clarificatio eorum, quae in occulto sunt corpore abscondita ... Et isto modo accepta anatomia non est scientia nec theorica nec pratica (!), sed operatio quaedam, etiam quae in vivo facta sit talis operatio manualis. Pro fine cuius intenditur forte sanitas, quia medicina nec quo ad practicam, nec quo ad theoricam est operari, sed scire operari et isto modo etiam Medicina est scientia ... Sed anatomia sic sumpta prout est instrumentum deserviens medicinae, non est scientia, sed tantum instrumentum."

75  Carpi 1521, 6v: "Alio modo capitur anatomia pro scientia et hoc dupliciter. Primo modo capitur pro scientia qua cognoscuntur membra tam simplicia quam composita et eorum operationes, compositiones, colligantiae, situs et huiusmodi. Et isto modo est pars medicinae theoricae et ei supponitur ... et isto modo supponitur etiam naturali philosophiae."

matters Avicenna considered them to belong to the theoretical part of medicine, and also Carpi concludes that anatomy forms a part of theoretical medicine. He. however, leaves open the question of whether anatomy defined this way can be called a science (*scientia*) or an art (*ars*).[76]

When discussing the qualities of an good anatomist, Carpi points out that the practioners of anatomy should rely more on their senses than on written words.[77] Galen is the only author who can be compared with sense-evidence. However, even the senses can be deceived and in these cases the anatomist must discuss the matter with the best trained anatomists available and compare their views.[78] Carpi's basic position in this matter is that sense knowledge takes priority over authorities. This becomes clear in his work on the bones of the human body where he notes that in anatomy the authorities are at fault, if they claim something to be contrary to the senses.[79]

In the 1530's and 1540's changes took place in anatomical teaching at the Universities of Padua and Bologna which had an impact on anatomical writing. Firstly, annual anatomical

---

76  Carpi 1521, 6v: "Alio modo capitur anatomia pro scientia cognitionis membrorum, ubi etiam traditur modus operandi cum manu actu et demonstrandi ipsa membra ... Et de hac Mundinus hic loquitur et supponitur medicinae practicae, pro quanto iuvat in cognoscendis membris et eorum complexionibus et compositionibus, et ita in cognoscendis causis aegritudinum et ut sic est pars Medicinae Theoricae; pro quanto vero confert in curandis aegritudinibus, est pars practicae. ... Sed pro quanto ego video Avicennam de eo loqui, ubi Theoricae loquitur. Ideo dico eam esse partem Medicinae Theoricae et hac sufficiant de diffinitione anatomiae. Utrum autem anatomia ut superius diffinita magis dicatur ars quam scientia, non est presentis negotii."

77  Carpi 1521, 6r: "Et non credat aliquis per solam vivam vocem aut per scripturam posse habere hanc disciplinam, quia hic requiritur visus et tactus."

78  Carpi 1521, 7v: "Credere tamen debet anatomes Gal. maxime concordante sensu aliter nec non aliis auctoritatibus est credendum, ubi experientia et sensus sunt in contrarium. Multi tamen sunt qui decipiuntur sensu seu unum pro alio capientes ex sua debili cogitativa. Non credat ergo aliquis sibi soli, sed communicet doctorum auctoritates et sui ipsius opinionem cum peritis in anatomia si potest. Et simul sit sensus et experientia super eo de quo sit sermo, ut quae forte non distinguit unus, distinguant forte alii. Et istis servatis aliquis poterit appellari bonus anatomes."

79  Carpi 1521, 413v: "Et dicat oppositum qui velit quia sensus sic est. Et in anatomia locus ab auctoritate contra sensum non habet veritatem." Of the distinction between reason and senses in Carpi's thought, see French 1985, 52–60.

153

dissections were performed, and achieved great success.[80] Secondly, as a result of his anatomical observations Andreas Vesalius published his *De humani corporis fabrica* in 1543. The illustrations in this manual were far more accurate than in previous books on anatomical matters (like Mondino's or Carpi's). Thirdly, botanical gardens were founded by the universities in Northern Italy, and thus the study of plants and herbs for medical purposes began.

The publication of Vesalius' work and the increased knowledge of anatomical matters led to several bitter disputes. These disputes have sometimes been treated as a controversy between the Aristotelians and the Galenists on some specific medical matter, like the circulation of the blood. However, these debates, can also be considered from a more profound point of view. At least in the latter part of the sixteenth century the Aristotelians and the medical writers differed in their views about the role of anatomy as a discipline and its suitability for a basis of the whole art of medicine. One such medical writer was Vesalius, who in the preface to his book emphasized the importance of sense perception for anatomical studies.

Bassiano Landi, who was the first ordinary professor of medical theory at the University of Padua between 1551–1563, defended the usefulness of anatomy to philosophers. He considered anatomy to be the other part of theoretical surgery.[81] He also stated that anatomy is a contemplative science, because it deals with the causes and uses of the parts of the human body.[82] Gabriele Falloppio, who lectured on surgery and anatomy at Padua between 1551–1562, treated the nature of anatomical discipline in his book concerning the bones. He noted that in the past authors had given

---

80  On these annual performances, see Bylebyl 1979 and Eriksson (ed.) 1959.
81  Landi, *Anatomiae corporis humani libri duo* 1605, 2: "Rursus Chirurgica theoretica in alias distribuitur partes: in urendi, secandi, fuendique partem et eam, quae singula hominis membra sua ratione exquirit, quae Anatome nuncupata est. Haec latius patet caeteris partibus et cognoscenda initio sese offert futuro chirurgo, adminiculatur etiam physico." On the professors of medical theory at the University of Padua between 1524 and 1611, see the list in Siraisi 1987, 92–93 (note 54).
82  Landi 1605, 4: "Anatome, qua de sermo nobis est, est singularum particularum extra intraque adiacentium corpus humanum, scientia contemplarix, quae causas ususque membrorum omnium vestigat. Huiusmodi Anatomen esse scientiam, nobis dari in praesentia petimus, non enim ignotum illud est."

the term "anatomy" two different meanings; first as a description of the actual dissection and, secondly, as an entire discipline with its own theory. According to Falloppio, anatomy has both a practical and a theoretical part and, what is most important, it is based on sense perception. What is first discovered by anatomists, can later be causally and theoretically proved by philosophers and physicians.[83]

During the second part of the century there appears a novel tendency to integrate new-found anatomical knowledge into the old Aristotelian system of natural philosophy. Hieronymus Fabricius ab Aquapendente and Girolamo Capodivacca are the two foremost representatives of this group of scholars. In his article about Fabricius' "Aristotle project", Andrew Cunningham deals with the aims and details of this project.[84] In his view Fabricius considered every proper anatomical account to have four parts: first dissection or *historia* of some part of any animal body; secondly investigation of the action of the part; thirdly an induction to discover the use or cause of it; and finally a demonstration of the validity of this cause.[85]

---

83  Gabriele Falloppio, *Expositio in librum Galeni de ossibus*, in *Opera omnia* 1584, 521: "Duae autem haec vox apud authores , praecipue apud Galenum, plurimis in locis significare videtur et actionem ipsam scilicet, qua animal secamus et aliquando non partialem illam divisionem, sed artem quandam communem, vel habitum, qui theoremata et conclusiones habet, quae reddunt hominem talem, ut optime instructus anatomicus dici possit ... Anatome est ars, vel habitus animi, quo optima cum theoria, id est speculatione, omnes vel minutissimas corporis internas, ac externas particulas dividere possumus: ob id, ut quae sensu in his partibus cognoscenda sunt, vere pateant ... Addidi in definitione ultimam particulam, ut quae sensu sunt cognoscenda recte pateant: quia in anatome nihil nisi quod sensu patet, percipiendum venit." Note also page 520 on the relationship between anatomy and philosophy or medicine: "Quae omnia, cum sensu fuerint percepta, sunt in causa ut philosophus facilius causas immutationum et differentias inquirat. Medicus autem illa tanquam probata et declarata, suscipit ab anatomico."

84  Cunningham defines his meaning of this "Aristotle project" in the following way: "an open-ended research programme on animals, devoted to the acquisition of true causal knowledge (*scientia*), on certain kinds of topic (not research "problems"), such as parts, organs and processes, and employing a thought-through and consistent methodology and epistemology, a suitable technical vocabulary, and the like. And when I talk of such an "Aristotle project" being practised in the late sixteenth century, I am referring to a deliberate and self-conscioud attempt to model new anatomical research on this kind of view of Aristotle's own practice." Cunningham 1985, 198.

85  Cunningham 1985, 216.

Even if anatomy deals with the particulars of the world, it is still an appropriate topic for the true philosopher. In fact, anatomy is a part of natural philosophy according to Fabricius. He explicitly notes that anatomy is nothing else than the true and solid basis of the whole of medicine, and the ultimate perfection and consummation of natural philosophy.[86] This Aristotelian investigation of natural philosophy is capable of being extended into new areas, however, and so, in Cunningham's view, it is not a set of problems, but a programme of research.[87] According to Cunningham, Fabricius' "Aristotle project" thereby offers an implicit contrast with other anatomical research projects being pursued by contemporary anatomists. He gives two major reasons for this: the other projects were centrally concerned with just one animal (man); and they were not philosophy as Fabricius understood it.[88]

In my view, Cunningham exaggerates somewhat the unique nature of Fabricius' aims. This can be shown by studying the texts of Fabricius' colleague at the University of Padua, Girolamo Capodivacca. Capodivacca (or Capivaccio), who held the second ordinary chair in practical medicine at Padua (1564–1589), wrote a treatise called *De anatomica methodo*, where he tried in a scholastic manner to establish anatomy on a sound and theoretically satisfying basis. He began the work traditionally by emphasizing the usefulness and necessity of anatomy for medicine in order to know the parts of the human body.[89] However, Capodivacca rejects the idea that anatomical method could simply be built on dissection, because anatomy deals also with the action and use of the parts of the human body. For him anatomical method is above all a mental habit, which is applied to the parts of the human body and their nature in order to reveal something that is hidden.[90] This

---

86  In the dedication to the book *On the larynx*, see Cunningham 1985, 202.

87  Cunningham 1985, 202–206. Also on page 211: "Fabricius is deliberately picking-up anatomical investigation at the point where he believed Aristotle had dropped it, and pursuing it in precisely the way he believed Aristotle had pursued it."

88  Cunningham 1985, 222.

89  Capodivacca Girolamo, *De anatomica methodo* in *Opera omnia* 1603, 14: "Unde locorum, seu partium corporis humani cognitionem ex anatomia petendam esse medicinam facturo planum est ... Utile ergo et necessarium nostrum est propositum."

90  Capodivacca 1603, 14: "Nam Anatome, seu anatomia est vox Graeca et apud Latinos sonat dissectio, seu consectio; secundum quem significatum nequa-

more valuable mental part of anatomy conducts the actual operation of surgeons, and helps us invent remedies from the nature of the things so found.[91]

Capodivacca discusses next the definition of anatomy. The most accurate definition in his view is the following: anatomy is a science (*scientia*) of man which has been equipped with a rational and voluntary movement is invented by medicine, dissection and action, and use for maintaining life.[92] The form of anatomy is science, which Capodivacca explicitly distinguishes from the practice of manual operations. The subject-matter of anatomy is the human being, which Capodivacca also deliberately distinguishes from the other animals.[93] Thus Capodivacca distances himself from those sixteenth-century anatomists, like Fabricius, who wanted to build a general anatomy of all animals. The addition "voluntary and rational movement" (*motus voluntarius rationalis*) in the subject-matter of anatomy further distinguishes anatomy from other parts of physiology which deal with elements, humours and so on. Capo-divacca defines maintaining life (*gratia indicationis vitalis*) as the end of anatomy. By this end anatomy and medicine in general are distinguished from philosophy. Philosophy also treats the human body in many ways, but never in order to maintain life.[94]

---

quam accipimus methodum anatomicam, cum ad anatomicum pertineat (ad differentiam lanii) non modo circa dissectionem versari, verum etiam circa actiones et usus. Quare de methodo anatomica idem ad partionem dicendum ... A simili igitur nos per methodum anatomicam intelligimus habitum in mente hominis, quem applicas huic et illi humano membro, illius membri naturam, alioqui abditam dignoscit."

91 Capodivacca 1603, 14: "Quare nos ... circa methodum anatomicam versabimur, ut duas propositas partes in se claudit; et potissimum quia et secunda pars, quamvis non conducat ad usum artis, ratione sectionis faciendae a chirurgo, attamen conducit artifici, et dignoscat locos affectos et sciat ex rei natura cognita invenire iuvantia."

92 Capodivacca 1603, 15: "Anatomia est scientia hominis, motu voluntario rationali praediti, a medico, sectione, actione et usu inventa, gratia indicationis vitalis."

93 Capodivacca 1603, 14: "Loco formae et proinde generis dictum fuit, esse *Scientiam*, ut distinguetur a peritia, quae pertinet ad incisores, ac manuales. Loco autem subiecti et proinde differentiae, dictum fuit, *Hominis*, ad differentiam Anatomiae versantis circa bruta."

94 Capodivacca 1603, 14: "Tum huius subiecti addita est ratio formalis: fuit autem *motus voluntarius rationalis*; ut per hanc particulam distingueretur Anatomia ut pars Physiologiae ... Ut propterea per hanc particulam distinguatur Anatomia ab ea physiologiae parte, quae verdsatur circa

What is noteworthy in Capodivacca's treatise is his emphasis on the rational basis of anatomical knowledge. The anatomical method is cognition, which is not only based on sense-perception but also on rational inference.[95] He wants to build an anatomical science, which is based on this rational, "anatomical method".[96] In this way his idea reminds me of Fabricius' "Aristotle project", but with the difference that Galen, not Aristotle, was the most notable past author on medical matters for Capodivacca. Another difference stems from the fact that Fabricius wanted to build a general anatomy of all animals, whereas Capodivacca confined himself to the anatomy of the human body.[97]

If we consider these sixteenth-century works on the nature of anatomy as a whole, it is possible to point out some general trends in their claims. First of all, most of these authors considered anatomy to be useful both for medicine and the philosophy of nature. Many of them treated anatomy as a part of medicine, properly belonging to the physiological part of that discipline. As we saw in the case of Fabricius, the Galenic idea that anatomy should consider the action and use of the parts of the body as well as their structure, was widely accepted among anatomical writers during that time.[98]

---

elementa, temperamenta et humores ... Tandem loco finis dictum fuit, *gratia indicationis vitalis*, ut per hanc particulam distingueretur facultas haec anatomia ac medica a philosophia. Siquidem et philosophus versatur circa corpus humanum, tum multifariam acceptum, tum ut est praeditum motu voluntario rationali, at nequaquam a philosopho consideratur gratia indicationis vitalis."

95  Capodivacca 1603, 14: "Primum igitur dictum fuit, *Methodus anatomica est cognitio*. Per quam intelligere oportet duplicem habitum, hoc est, non modo sensu, sed etiam ratione comparatum. Nec ab re. Nam cum facultas anatomica sit pars medicinae et medicina sit cognitio ratione comparata: huiusmodi etiam erit facultas anatomica ... Ob id huius caussae cognitio et habitus ille, non erit peritia, sed scientia."

96  Andrew Wear discusses in an interesting article the relationship of the sixteenth century anatomical writers to William Harvey's methodological considerations. See Wear 1983.

97  William Edwards has interpreted Capodivacca to precede Zabarella in the attempt to combine the philosophical and medical methods and traditions at the University of Padua. Edwards 1976, 302–303. However, my present study tries to show that the practical intention and the concept of science of Capodivacca and other medical writers were quite different from Zabarella's, in spite of some verbal similarities in scientific terminology.

98  As Jerome J. Bylebyl has shown, however, the present meaning of the words anatomy and physiology as "structure" and "function", does not very well correspond to the Renaissance use of these terms. Bylebyl 1985b, 224.

Secondly, as a result of the above definition of anatomy, it was not merely considered as an art (*ars*) which deals just with manual operations (dissections), but as a science (*scientia*) which considers the uses or causes of the parts of human – and animal – bodies. Thirdly, as against the medieval manuals of anatomy, the basic textbook on the subject was not a commentary which bookishly discussed the views of ancient authors, but above all these sixteenth-century writers emphasized the empirical foundation of all anatomical knowledge. They felt anatomy should be based on sense-perception, and where the past authors and the present senses were at odds with each other, the anatomist should believe his senses instead of old books. As a result of all these tendencies, anatomy gradually came to be considered an autonomous discipline which could challenge the place of natural philosophy as the basis of all medical studies.[99] Next we shall look at what kind of response Aristotelian philosophers, like Zabarella, had to offer in warding off this threat.

## 6.4. Zabarella's response to medical humanism

The distinction between theoretical sciences and practical or productive disciplines in Zabarella's philosophy assumes a more concrete form when we deal with the relationship between natural philosophy and medicine. Nowhere else in his philosophy is the distinction between theory and practice drawn so clearly, because while in subject matter these disciplines were close to each other, in their essence and methodology they were far apart.

A lively discussion on the relationship between medicine and natural philosophy was already in progress amongst the Paduan Aristotelians even before Zabarella wrote on the subject. Marcantonio Zimara divided the arts and sciences in the Aristotelian manner, and pointed out clearly that medicine is an art, not a science, unless the latter word is employed in an improper

---

99 On this progress, see Bylebyl 1979, 363–365. Jacques Roger notes that even if the Paduan anatomists criticized some features of Aristotle's teaching, they stuck to basic Aristotelian concepts of natural philosophy, such as the four elements. See Roger 1976.

sense.[100] According to Zimara, medicine adopts its principles from natural philosophy; both of which disciplines consider the same subject matter, but differ in their method of consideration. Natural science consider health as a passion of a natural entity, but in medicine health is seen as an operational thing, which is to be conserved.[101] Moreover, in contrast to the other disciplines, the distinction between theory and practice in medicine is relative because they are so closely connected. The "theoretical" physician must know the "practice" and the "practical" physician must understand theory. Thus for Zimara any distinction between theory and practice in medicine is only accidental and equivocal.[102]

Even if medicine adopts its principles from natural philosophy, it is not subalternated to the philosophy of nature in Zimara's view. There are two kinds of subalternation, firstly on the ground of the principles and, secondly, on the ground of subject matter.

---

100 Zimara, *Theoremata* 1556, prop.38 (*Scientia est necessarium cognitio*), 24r: "Unde verum genus medicinae est ars, non scientia ... unde medicina proprie est ars. Scientia autem est (communiter sumendo nomen scientiae, non proprie), ut bene notavit Galenos ibi quod nomen scientiae communiter et non proprie audire oportet." Also prop. 52 (*Principium in cognitione est finis in operatione et principium operationis est finis in cognitione*), 42v: "Nam cum medicina sit ars factiva, non nam scientia nisi communiter dici potest, quia scientia ut distinguitur contra alios habitus intellectus ab Aristo." Zimara makes the same definition in his *Tabulae* (*Medicina est ars operatrix*), 96r: "Medicina est ars operatrix inventa ratione et experimento, conservans sanitatem et removens aegritudinem. Et haec est veracior diffinitio, quae in aliquo librorum alicuius Averrois fuit inventa. 6.colliget, cap.1."

101 Zimara 1565, 95v: "Medicina sumit principia sua a scientia naturali: et quando aliquid commune in utraque scientia istarum consideratur, consideratur duobus modis diversis. Sanitas enim et aegritudo considerantur in scientia naturalis, ut sunt passiones entium naturalium. Medicina vero considerat de eis, ut unam earum conservet, et reliquam destruat."

102 Zimara 1556, prop. 82, 53v: "Medicina quae a toto genere practica est, licet secundum similitudinem aliquid eius dicatur practicum et aliquid speculativum ... Secus autem est de theorico et practico, quae dividunt Medicinam, quia tales sunt differentiae accidentales in Medicina. Unde theoricum et practicum, quae dividunt scientiam in communi aequivoce dicuntur cum theorico et practico per quae dividiturMedicina, quia impossibile est easdem esse differentias, per quas dividitur superius et inferius, unde theoricum in Medicina ordinatur ad practicum, non sic autem est de theorico et practico per quae dividitur scientia in communi, quia scientiae speculativae non sunt propter practicas, ut patet ex proemio Metaphy." See also Antonaci 1978, 38–40, and on Zimara's medical thought in general Antonaci 1983.

The subalternation must fulfil both conditions. Medicine does adopt its principles from natural philosophy, but does not consider the same subject matter in the same way, as we saw above. Zimara concludes that a real subalternative science must also be a speculative science, but medicine is only an art.[103] Nevertheless, the art of medicine helps nature to reach its ends. Health can be achieved with the help of medicine and in this respect medicine can be said to subalternate natural philosophy, like alchemy and agriculture does.[104] Zimara considers medicine and natural philosophy as two sisters: medicine is the body of natural philosophy and natural philosophy is the mind of medicine, like Boethius had said. However, their family ties do not make them equal. As the mind is nobler than the body, so natural philosophy is nobler than medicine; as Aristotle said in his *Ethics*.[105]

---

103 Zimara 1556, prop. 82 (*Scientia quae subalternatur speculativae, speculativa est*), 53v: "Similiter etiam medicina, quae a toto genere practica est, licet secundum similitudinem aliquid eius dicatur practicum et aliquid speculativum, subalternatur merito principiorum scientiae Naturali, quae est speculativa. Et ex hoc patet error Conciliatoris et aliorum asserentium medicinam esse vere subalternatam scientiae Naturali." See also prop. 47 (*Scientiae speculativae sunt duobus modis ...*), 68r: "Et similiter medicina, quae est scientia factiva subalternatur Philosophiae naturali merito principiorum. Naturalis enim est sanitatis et aegritudinis prima investigare principia, ut testatur Aristoteles in lib. de Sensu et Sensato, hinc est quod ubi desinit Physicus, inde incipit Medicus." In a short *quaestio* called "*An medicina sit subalternata philosophiae*" also Santorio Santorio dealt with the question of subalternation of medicine under philosophy of nature. He denied this subalternation on the same grounds than Zimara. Santorio, *Commentaria in primam fen primi libri Canonis Avicennae* in *Opera omnia III*, 140c–141b.
104 Zimara 1556, prop. 82, 53v: "Omnium natura operatrix, Medicus vero minister, quia ex aliqua naturali virtute Sanitas perficitur auxilio artis, ideo propter quid in operatione artis oportet accipere, ex proprietatibus rerum naturalium et propter hoc Medicina subalternatur Philosophiae naturali, sicut Alchimia et agricultura et aliae huiusmodi. Et sic patet qualiter aliquae scientiae operativae subalternari possunt alicui scientiae mere speculativae secundum se et secundum omnes sui partes."
105 Zimara 1556, prop. 82, 53v: "Sic finis Naturalis scientiae sapit et ostendit alium modum considerandi Medicinae, unde Aristoteles istas duas scientias sorores appellabat et alteram describebat per alteram; dicebat nam Medicinam esse corporis Philosophiam et philosophia dicebat esse animi Medicinam, nam ut inquit divinus Boethius in 4.consolatione philosophica. Animorum salus quid est nisi virtus et aegritudo quid nisi vitium et adverte, quod quanto anima praestantior est corpore, tanto Philosophia, quae instituit animum, praestantior est Medicina, quae instituit corpus, ut dicit Aristoteles in 1. Ethicorum cap. 17."

Of the Paduan Aristotelians Jacopo Zabarella was perhaps the author who discussed the relationship between philosophy of nature and medical art most thoroughly. Like Zimara, he did not consider medicine to be subalternated to the philosophy of nature, but unlike him, Zabarella did not consider the distinction between theoretical and practical medicine accidental. He wanted to consider the whole art of medicine as an operational art.[106] In spite of medicine's prominent place among the arts, Zabarella sharply denies its scientific status. According to him, those writers err who claim that medicine is a science. It is enough to admit that it is the noblest of all arts.[107] Zabarella also attacks those writers, who place medicine alongside the philosophy of nature among the sciences. What is even worse, many medical men even dare to consider medicine better than natural philosophy as regards knowledge of the human body, simply because a physician has treated it in a more specific way than a natural philosopher. They claim, because of this, that medicine is necessary for philosophers in order that they might to treat all scientific things perfectly.[108]

According to Zabarella, the situation is, in fact, quite the contrary. Contemplative philosophy does not adopt anything from the productive arts, but rather the arts adopt everything from philosophy. When intellectual cognition is said to be knowledge through its causes, this concerns only contemplative philosophy in Zabarella's view. Neither the art of medicine nor its singular parts can be considered science. No matter how valuable and precise medicine may be it could never be a science because it is not practised for the sake of knowledge, but for a production, that

---

106 In order to understand the relationship between the philosophy of nature and medicine as Zabarella saw it, we must keep in mind what kind of knowledge, according to him, is sufficient for each type of discipline. On this point see chapter 2.2.

107 Zabarella 1597, 36d: "Medicinam quidem scientiam esse non dicemus et falluntur medici, qui id audent asservare. Satis habeant, quum effectricem artem exerceant, si eam caeteris artibus praestare fateamur."

108 Zabarella 1597, 60a–b: "Quo factum est, ut plures medici apparente et inani argumento decepti non modo medicinam scientiam esse contemplativam, sed etiam in humani corporis cognitione Philosophiae naturali praeferendam affirmare ausi fuerint. Siquidem diligentior omnium partium nostri corporis consideratio fit a medico, quam a Philosopho. Quamobrem dicunt, Philosopho necessariam esse medicam artem, ut perfectus fiat et plenam rerum scientiam assequatur."

is, that health can be maintained or restored to the human body.[109]

If knowledge of the human body is considered purely for its own sake, not for curative purposes, it should be called natural science rather than medicine. In Zabarella's view if something is called medicine, it cannot anymore be called a science.[110] Even if it would be admitted, that medicine could be practised for knowledge's sake, it could not be called a pure science, because it does not explain the first causes and without this knowledge the other causes cannot be clearly known. A physician does not deal with the nature of prime matter and, without this knowledge, he might accept some accident as a form, because it seems to be sufficient in regard to that knowledge which is needed in medicine.[111]

The first, physiological part of medicine teaches us that a human being is constituted of four humours and elements in Zabarella's view. It also deals with parts and uses of the human body, most of which are also common to other, lower animals. Thus in contrast to the rest of medicine, physiology does not give us knowledge of a human being primarily as a human being, but only as an animal among the other animals.[112] According to

---

109 Zabarella 1597, 60c–e: "Quo fit, ut Philosophus contemplativus a nulla arte sumat rei alicuius cognitionem, sed potius ab ipso artes omnes. Loquor autem de cognitione intellectuali per causas acquisita, haec enim solius Philosophi contemplativi propria est. Dicimus itaque non modo medicinam totam non posse scientiam dici, sed neque illam eius partem, in qua de elementis, de humoribus, de partibus humani corporis earumque natura et usu disseritur. Idque ostendimus primum quidem ratione scopi ac finis illius tractationis. Sit enim quantumvis diligens et exquisita, non est scientia, quia non scientiae gratia fit, sed operationis, ut corporis sanitatem, vel conservare, vel recuperare valeamus."

110 Zabarella 1597, 60e: "Quod si quis dicat, partem illam etiam sciendi tantum gratia legi posse, non gratia medendi. Tunc sequitur, eam non amplius esse vocandam medicinae partem, sed pars erit scientiae naturalis. Satis est igitur, si quatenus est artis medicae, eatenus scientia dici non potest."

111 Zabarella 1597, 60f: "Sed praeterea quocunque modo ea pars sumatur, etiamsi sciendi gratia scripta esse dicatur, scientia dici non potest; tum quia primas causas non declarat, quibus ignoratis aliae propinquiores bene cognosci non possunt. Ad primam enim materiam eiusque naturam medicus non pervenit, neque fortasse veram formam cognoscit, sed accidens aliquod pro forma accipit, quum id ad artem illam et cognoscendam et exercendam ei sufficere videtur."

112 Zabarella 1597, 61b–c: "Docet enim hominem ex quatuor elementis et ex quatuor humoribus esse constitutum, tractat de partibus humani corporis, ac de earum usu, quae omnia vel eorum magna pars in brutis quoque animalibus inspiciuntur; quare homini primo et prout homo est non competunt."

Zabarella, Galen and other medical writers ought not to be criticized, because they wrote about medicine in the sake for curative purposes rather than knowledge for knowledge. One should only condemn those who place the art of medicine before the philosophy of nature, because there is nothing valuable to be known about the human body that natural philosophy has not treated.[113]

> If we consider within natural philosophy not only those things which have already been written, but also those which can be written and which belong to the perfect knowledge of all natural things that is possible to understand by means of proper human reason, no additional help is needed from the art of medicine for attaining knowledge of these things. On the contrary a physician takes entirely from a natural philosopher all that which is necessary for knowing and curing the parts of the human body.[114]

In the books on the methods (*De methodis*) Zabarella deals even more profoundly with the question of the relationship between natural philosophy and medicine. The whole art of medicine – both the operative and the educational part – requires some foreknowledge of the subject matter; that is the parts of a human body and their functions. Zabarella asks how a physician can cure a sick body if he does not know its parts.[115] The end of medicine is maintaining health and recovering it, if lost; however in Zabarella's view health cannot be known and this end cannot be achieved if a physician does not know all the parts of a human body and their nature, composition, purpose and function. He repeats, however, that medicine lacks the perfec-

---

113  Zabarella 1597, 61d: "Qui vero artem medicam scientiae naturali audent anteponere, ridiculi sunt; quia nihil est cognitu dignum in humano orpore, quod non a Philosopho naturali cognoscatur."

114  Zabarella 1597, 61f–62a: "Propterea si naturalem Philosophiam non eam solum sumamus, quae scripta est, sed eam, quae scribi potest et quae rerum omnium naturalium perfectam cognitionem tradat, quantam homo proprio ingenio invenire et capere potest, illa nullo medicae artis auxilio indiget pro rerum cognitione adipiscenda, sed contra potius medicus a Philosopho naturali ea omnia sumit, quae pro cognitione partium humani corporis ab eo sanandi sunt ipsi necessaria."

115  Zabarella 1597, 193e–194e.

tion of natural philosophy because it does not deal with prime matter and substantial form.[116]

What is even more interesting in Zabarella's discussion is his treatment of the ways foreknowledge of medical art can be acquired. He recognizes two different ways in which a physician can know the parts of a human body. Firstly, he learns through perceptible knowledge and anatomical observations, thereby knowing the matters in his discipline without a knowledge of their reasons. Secondly, a physician can know the reasons which lie behind what he sees, the knowledge of which he achieves from natural philosophy.[117] Zabarella thinks that Aristotle made the same distinction in his books the *History of Animals* and the *Parts of animals*. In the first one he relies on sense-perception to classify the different parts of animals. In the second work, Aristotle offers causal explanations for that which he considers. In Zabarella's view this order of understanding results from our own inability to comprehend everything at once. It is thus better to progress gradually from confuse knowledge to distinct knowledge.[118] Even the medical writers seem to admit that knowledge of all natural things and their causes belongs to the philosophy of nature when they call the first part of medicine "physiology" (*fysiologiken*), even though they do not emphasise the scientific nature of this treatment.[119]

---

116 Zabarella 1597, 195e–196f: "Ad primam autem materiam et substantialem formam medicus non pervenit, quia harum cognitione non eget, propterea medicina cadit a perfectione scientiae speculativae."

117 Zabarella 1597, 196f: "Videtur autem duplici via medicus uti ad cognoscendas humani corporis partes. Una quidem per sensum et per anatomen, qua sine causarum cognitione rem ita esse cognoscit. Altera vero per rationem, quam ex naturali philosophia desumit."

118 Zabarella 1597, 197a–b: "Sic etenim Aristotelem quoque de animalium partibus disservisse conspicimus. Rem namque varietatis ac difficultatis plenam esse cognoscens, operae pretium fore duxit, si harum rerum historiam praemitteret, in qua sine causarum redditione id solum, quod experientia ipsa ostendere potuit, de animalium partibus doceret. Deinde vero in libris De partibus animalium rationem reddit eorum omnium, quae simplici enarratione in libris De historia exposuerat. Ea namque est ingenii nostri imbecillitas, ut non statim integram rei notitiam capessere valeamus, sed gradatim progrediamur et a cognitione quod sit, quam confusam vocant, ad cognitionem cur sit, quae distincta dicitur, transeamus."

119 Zabarella 1597, 197e–f: "Quod videntur medici omnes confiteri, dum primam hanc medicinae partem fysiologiko appellant, quasi non proprie medicinalem, sed a naturali philosophia desumtam, licet non amplius naturalis, vel scientialis ea tractatio dici possit."

The subject matter of medicine involves maintaining or recovering health only in human beings, not in animals. Since the whole discipline deals only with human body it cannot be a science. Its subject matter is, however, proper to the function and end of an art. What a natural philosopher writes about animals, a medical writer must apply to human beings. He moves from the universal and scientific discussion of natural philosophy to a consideration of its particular and artistic aspects from the standpoint of operation, not knowledge. In Zabarella's view Averroes was right when he noted this in his book *Colliget*, where he said that medical treatments are neither scientific nor demonstrative because the sentences used in them are not universal as such (*per se*), but only illustrate universal things in particular subject matter.

According to Zabarella natural philosophy and medicine differ not only in respect of their ends and subject matter, but also in their methods are different. As we have seen, the resolutive method is proper to medicine and the compositive method proper to the philosophy of nature. In Zabarella's view a physician does not use proper demonstrations or, if he does, he takes them from natural philosophy. In medical art the resolutive order of presentation proceeds from knowledge to cure. The end, that is maintaining or recovering health, is broken down into principles, on which the operation is then based.[120]

In the order of presentation Zabarella wants to differentiate between the presentation of a whole discipline and a part of it. For example, the first part of the art of medicine, physiology, has a compositive order as against medicine as a whole, which is arranged according to a resolutive order. This goes to show that physiology is not really medicine at all, but natural philosophy, because in physiology the nature of the human body is contemplated apart from operation. To illustrate his claim, Zabarella presents a comparison between a human being and his eye. Because the whole human being is an animal, it is not necessary for an eye to be an animal, too. An eye is animal only as a part of human being, but not in itself. Correspondingly in the singular parts of a discipline the orders of presentation are not always

---

120  Zabarella 1597, 198a–e.

resolutive or compositive, but ought to be named only on the basis of the whole habit, whose parts they are.[121]

Zabarella compares Galen's, Avicenna's and Averroes' treatments of the nature of medical knowledge. In Zabarella's view, Averroes wanted to point out at the very beginning of his *Colliget*, that medicine is an art and not a science. He proceeds to claim that the principles of knowledge cannot be demonstrated in the same discipline, but either must be naturally known or must be adopted from some other discipline. This latter is the case of medicine, where the principles are taken from natural philosophy.[122] Avicenna also treated medicine in the resolutive order, according to Zabarella. In Avicenna's view the operative order in medical art is always contrary to the doctrinal order. Where knowledge ends, there the operation begins, both in universal and particular knowledge. They both end in cure, which is the beginning of operation. The order Galen used in his *Ars medica* is also resolutive, according to Zabarella. This book can be divided into two parts. The first part proceeds from the knowledge of principles to the knowledge of subject matter and its end. The second part moves to the principles of things and remedies, which is actually a resolutive order of presentation.[123]

Galen well understood the nature of medicine. If a science is spoken of in the widest sense of the term to mean all human cognition, he felt, medicine can be called a science. Yet, according to Zabarella, this is not a proper definition of medicine, because it does not express clearly the nature and essence of medical discipline. Even if all arts are practised on some knowledge, their nature does not consist of this knowledge, but of operation, at which the whole of knowledge aims. In Zabarella's view the fault of Galen's definition is that it does not speak of this operation at all. This is why Zabarella prefers Avicenna's definition, according to which medicine is cognition of the human body in the light of health and sickness. In this definition knowledge is connected to the final end of medicine, which is the maintenance of health and curing of its absence.[124]

---

121  Zabarella 1597, 222c–223a.
122  Zabarella 1597, 199b–200d.
123  Zabarella 1597, 208a–209e.
124  Zabarella 1597, 210e–211a.

The best definition of all, however, is the one presented by Averroes. According to this, medicine is an operative art which proceeds from principles and aims at maintaining the health of the human body and curing its sickness. If we consider Galen's definition closely, we notice that it concerns the philosophy of nature rather than medicine. It is the natural philosopher who wants to know all natural beings, their accidental qualities, along with the symptoms and causes of their health or sickness.[125]

Zabarella considers that Aristotle wrote a book of health and sickness, too, of which remains nothing but a small fragment.[126] According to Zabarella, this tractate is not about medicine but natural philosophy, because the knowledge of any natural things is part of the philosophy of nature and no operation follows from this knowledge. When we aim at operation, the knowledge of natural beings belongs to an art, not a science.[127] The difference between medicine and natural philosophy in regard to health and sickness is explained by Averroes in the first chapter of his *Colliget*.[128] An art must always be defined in terms of an operation, whereas natural science must be defined solely in terms of cognition. Thus Galen's definition of medicine is not good enough according to Zabarella, because it refers to neither art nor operation.[129]

The question of the relationship between the philosophy of nature and medicine also arose in Zabarella's *De rebus naturalibus*, in which he dealt with the natural sciences. He points

---

125  Zabarella 1597, 211c: "Idcirco optima est definitio tradita ab Averroe in primo capite primi libri: Medicina est ars operatrix exiens a principiis veris, in qua quaeritur conservatio sanitatis corporis humani et remotio suae aegritudinis. Definitio autem Galeni, si bene consideretur, ad philosophum naturalem potius, quam ad medicum pertinet. Philosophus enim naturalis res omnes naturales cognoscere vult, earumque accidentia omnia, etiam sanitatem et morbum et horum signa et causas."

126  Charles B. Schmitt has considered the question whether Aristotle really wrote any medical works. See Schmitt 1985, 2–3.

127  Zabarella 1597, 211d: "Ideo Aristoteles libellum scripsit de sanitate et morbo, cuius parvum fragmentum tantummodo habemus, reliqua desiderantur. Quem librum non debemus medicum appellare, sed naturalem, quia cognitio cuiuscunque rei naturalis, quaecunque illa sit, ad naturalem philosophum pertinet, dum nulla nostra operatio cognitionem illam consecuta est. Sed cognitio alicuius rei naturalis, quae ad aliquam nostram operationem dirigatur, non amplius ad naturalem philosophiam, sed ad artem aliquam pertinet."

128  Zabarella refers here to *Ars medica*, which must be a lapse.

129  Zabarella 1597, 211e–212b.

out again that the art of medicine adopts its physiology from the philosophy of nature. If the medical writers want to know the anatomy of the human body, they must therefore follow Aristotle methodologically. Zabarella points out that they should not study the *History of Animals*, but the *Parts of Animals*, which methodologically shows us the functions of different parts of the bodies in question.[130]

There is a fine borderline between medicine and natural philosophy in their respective treatment of health and sickness. The difference lies both in subject matter and cause. Zabarella repeats that medicine confines itself to the health and sickness of human beings, whereas natural philosophy concerns itself with all natural beings. The causes in medicine are equally foreign to natural philosophy because, for the most part, they are remedies, which are discovered by the examination of medicinal plants. A physician investigates plants in order to maintain or restore health in the human body. A natural philosopher, however, treats plants quite differently, examining their nature and qualities in order to gain a perfect knowledge of them.[131]

Zabarella's conclusion about the relationship between the art of medicine and natural philosophy is that the latter must consider the universal qualities of health and sickness, while the former concentrates on finding remedies for particular diseases. Aristotle's fragment on health and sickness is therefore on the borderline between these disciplines. Zabarella sums this up in the saying: Where the art of medicine begins, there natural philosophy's universal consideration of sickness and health ends. From this point the physician descends to the treatment of all

---

130 Zabarella 1590, 84b–c: "Ex hac potissimum naturalis philosophiae parte sumit ars medica partem illam, quae physiologica dicitur, in qua de humano corpore ac de eius partibus sermo sit, quum Medico illas curaturo necessaria penitus sit earum cognitio. Ob id Medici, qui artificiosam ac fructuosam facere volunt humani corporis anatomen, imitari Aristotelem debent, non in libris historia, sed in libris de partibus methodice de ipsis partibus agentem."

131 Zabarella 1590, 90d–91a,117c–d: "Vires enim et proprietates plantarum medicinales cognoscendae sunt et a Medico et a Philosopho naturali, diversis tamen scopis. Medicus eas considerat, dum sibi proponit sanitatem recuperandam, vel conservandam. Philosophus autem naturalis eas inquirit, ut plenam habeat cognitionem plantarum, quae sunt species corporis naturalis, ideo id ei facere non convenit in libro de sanitate et morbo, sed solum in libris de plantis."

particular diseases and to knowledge of their causes.[132]

Zabarella makes a comparison between the relationship of these two disciplines, and that of moral philosophy and legislation. In the disciplines of ethics and politics, habits, virtues, vices and prescribing the laws are considered as universal doctrines, whereas the legislators prescribe laws for all particular things, with the aim of making human beings act virtuously.[133] As you cannot be a good physician without the knowledge of natural philosophy, so you cannot be a good legislator without moral philosophy. There is, however, one difference between these disciplines. Natural philosophy aims only at knowledge and medicine at operation, while both the disciplines of moral philosophy and legislation aim at action. These latter two are therefore both referred to as medicine of mind, with the difference that moral disciplines deal only with the universal while legislation descends to the particular.[134]

Zabarella wants further to distinguish legislation (*legislatoria*) from judicature (*iudiciaria*), the latter of which is some kind of knowledge of legal matters by those people who want to call themselves jurists (*iuriconsulti*). Plato in his *Gorgias* and Aristotle in his *Rhetorics* had already pointed out that judicature is not as noble as legislation because it only represents an acquaintance with legal matters, and therefore cannot be called an art, prudence or a science. According to Zabarella it is impossible that somebody could be well acquainted with legal matters without any knowledge of moral philosophy or legislation. In his view judicature

---

132 Zabarella 1590, 91e–g: "Ob id eam ego puto esse rationem, cur dicat Aristoteles tractationem de sanitate et aegritudine esse quodammodo in confinio scientiae naturalis et artis medicae. In ea desinere naturalem scientiam, ab ea vero medicam artem exordium sumere. Desinit enim Philosophus naturalis in universali consideratione sanitatis et morbi, a qua exordiens medicus descendit postea ad particularem morborum omnium tradendam notitiam et propriarum causarum."

133 Zabarella 1590, 92a–b.

134 Zabarella 1590, 92b–c: "Quamobrem sicuti bonus medicus esse non potest, qui non sit philosophus naturalis; ita nec bonus legislator, qui non calleat moralem philosophiam. Inter eas tamen illud interest, quod medicina solam effectionem respicit, philosophia naturalis non effectionem, sed solam scientiam. Civilis autem et legislatoria ambae ad actionem diriguntur, quo sit ut utramque liceat animae medicinam appellare, cum eo tamen discrimine, quod civilis universalia praecepta tradit, legislatoria vero descendit ad particularia."

should belong under legislation just as medication (*empirica*) belongs under the art of medicine.[135]

Against this background it is difficult to understand William Edwards' claim that Zabarella was the first sixteenth century Paduan writer to combine the medical and philosophical traditions after they had been divided for almost a century.[136] When Zabarella speaks about the relationship of medicine to natural philosophy in the middle of a work on methods, Edwards takes his methodology as a starting-point for his interpretation. If we realize, however, that the methodology is used only in order to illustrate the basic difference between these two kinds of disciplines, we end up with a different conclusion. It can be said that Zabarella agreed with Leoniceno, for example, in pointing out that Galen did not speak about research methods, but about orders of presentation in his *Ars medica.* Yet this approach misses the whole intention of Zabarella's treatment, which shows that his fundamental assumptions about the nature and role of theoretical and practical knowledge were quite different from those of the anatomists or medical commentators.

As we have seen, Zabarella did not appreciate any knowledge that could not fulfil the requirements of a science and therefore, according to him, medical art could never be one. He considered not only the subject matter, but the methods and ends of arts and sciences to be completely different. While discussing the principles of medical art Zabarella compares the anatomical principles with the principles derived from natural philosophy. In his view only the philosophy of nature, not anatomy, can provide a solid basis for medical practioners. In this respect Zabarella cannot be considered as a forerunner of modern experimental science.[137]

---

135 Zabarella 1590, 92c–d: "Aliud autem est legislatoria, aliud iudiciaria, quae est illa iurisperitia, quam profitentur illi, qui his temporia iuriconsulti appellari volunt. Hanc enim legislatoria ignobiliorem esse manifestum est, idque aperte testantur Plato in Gorgia et Aristoteles in primo libro de arte Rhetorica. Est enim simplex quaedam peritia, quae nec scientia, nec prudentia, nec ars appellari meretur, quum sine ratione sit; hanc enim callere aliquis potest absque ulla civilis, ac legislatoriae cognitione ... Sed ita videtur esse sub legislatoria, ut empirica sub arte medica."

136 Edwards 1976, 302–303.

137 Schmitt 1969 and Rossi 1983 end up with a similar conclusion. Schmitt, however, lays more weight upon those observations Zabarella makes about natural processes; but as Rossi points out, these are not used as experiments in

Once again his confidence in human intelligence to produce necessary science – and in the relevance of this science as a principle of human practical endeavours – is evident.

After Zabarella's *Opera logica* appeared, medical writers, were more modest in their attempts to place medicine among the theoretical sciences. This is obvious for example in Santorio Santorio's commentaries on Avicenna's *Canon* and Galen's *Ars medica*.[138] In the former, Santorio first discusses different opinions about the nature of medical knowledge; then, having denied medicine is a proper science, he admits that it can be called a science in a improper sense, just as Aristotle himself sometimes called arts as sciences.[139] In the commentary on Galen's *Ars medica*, too, Santorio points out clearly that Aristotle, Galen and Averroes agreed unianimously, that medicine could be called a science only in the wider, not in the proper meaning of the word.[140]

For Santorio, however, the definition of medicine as an art was not a reason to reject anatomy as a basis of medical knowledge. As well as Paterno, he had some reservations about the suitability of Aristotle's works on natural philosophy for a practising physician. In his quaestio *An anatomia pertineat ad medicum* (Should anatomy pertain to the physician?) Santorio emphasized the dependence of natural philosophy on sense perception. He also allowed that anatomy is not excusively a matter of perception, but

---

order to verify or falsify some idea, but only as an illustration of some Aristotelian point of view. Rossi 1983, 146.

138 Santorio Santorio (1561–1636) was professor of theoretical medicine at Padua between 1611 and 1624. On the life and works of Santorio, see Siraisi 1987, 206 and Grmek 1975, 101–104.

139 Santorio, *Commentaria in primam Fen primi libri Canonis Avicennae*, in *Opera omnia III* 1660, 41: "Quare concludimus, medicinam proprie esse artem et non scientiam, nisi dicamus, medicinam communiter et improprie esse vocatam scientiam, quia improprie enim Aristoteles 3.coeli text.61 artes vocat scientias. Ibi enim dicit, finem effectivae scientiae non esse scire, sed esse opus: ecce quod artes ab Aristotele vocantur scientiae effectivae, sed improprie quidem."

140 Santorio, *Commentaria in Artem medicinalem Galeni* 1602, 62–67. Also on page 14: "Respondetur, Galenum sumpsisiïse scientiam lato modo, pro quadam cognitione communi scientiae et arti. Quod haec responsio sit consona doctrinae Galeni, ex eo patet, quia ab ipso medicina inscribitur ars medicinalis et non scientia medicinalis. Insuper libro de constitutione artis cap. primo docet, medicinam esse artem et non scientiam."

is based on rational inference as well.[141] Santorio pointed out the scientific status of anatomy and saw it as a part of medicine, not of natural philosophy. For him the anatomical controversies that were going on during the sixteenth century were a sufficient guarantee of anatomy's status as a science involving reasoning as well as observation.[142]

The function of anatomy as the basis of medicine was also determinedly denied at the beginning of seventeenth century at Padua. In his *Apologia*, Cesare Cremonini vigorously attacked those medical writers who thought that anatomy was a science that could be compared with the philosophy of nature. Since all arts are made for the use for some other discipline, he believed the art of anatomy is primarily made for natural philosophy and only secondarily for medicine; above all for surgery.[143] According to Cremonini the art of anatomy is useful and perfect only when it fulfils the duties given to it. Thus it is ridiculous to maintain that anatomy would be perfect when it has found some minor muscle, gland or cavity that nobody else has found before. These kind of discoveries are no use for the natural philosophy, which is the proper end of anatomy. If intellect and rational deduction are

---

141  Santorio, *Commentaria in primam fen primi libri Canonis Avicennae* 1660, 144c–145a: "Nos dicimus anatomiam non consistere solum in membrorum visione, sed etiam in ratiocinio, quod versatur circa membrorum substantiam ... circa officia et usus omnium partium, circa exordia et compositiones, quae omnia licet sensui magna ex parte obiiciantur ... Praeterea non valet, hoc sensu cognoscitur sine ratiocinio, ergo non pertinet ad philosophum vel medicum; quia innumerabilia sunt, quae solum sensu cognoscuntur, quae tamen pertinent ad philosophum ... Idem dicimus in medicina plurima cognosci sensu tantum quae revera pertinent ad medicinam vel philosophiam."

142  Santorio 1660, 145b–c: "Sed concludimus anatomiam cognosci ratiocinio. Si enim sensu solo anatomia cognosceretur, non essent tot quaestiones in anatomia, quae a Laurentio considerantur et ante Laurentium a Vesalio et ab infinitis aliis ... quare manifeste falsa est illa sententia quod anatomia solum sensu sine ratiocinio intelligatur." See also Siraisi 1987, 327–328.

143  Cremonini, *Apologia dictorum Aristotelis de origine et principatu membrorum adversus Galenum* 1627, 51: "Nullus dicet esse artem per se ipsam, quia esset prope modum fatuum dissecare cadavera, solum ut illa essent dissecta et propter nihil aliud. Conveniunt omnes, quod sit ad alterius Artisusum. Cum sit igitur ordinata ad aliud, potest ordinari ad naturalem contemplationem ... Ars igitur dissectionis est ad usum naturalis contemplationis; est postea etiam ad usum Medicinae, praesertim Chirurgicae eo modo, quo dictum est."

overlooked and not allowed to help the senses, we are condemned to end up with errors in anatomical knowledge.[144]

Charles B. Schmitt takes Zabarella and Cremonini as examples of two types of Aristotelianism present at the University of Padua in the late sixteenth century. According to Schmitt, Zabarella strongly emphasized observation of the external world as a source of knowledge, while at the same time stressing that reason – not Aristotle – is the ultimate foundation of valid knowledge. Aristotle's authority is acceptable for Zabarella only insofar it is derived from reason, which is the final court of appeal.[145] On the other hand, in Schmitt's view, Cremonini considered himself merely an interpreter of the truth that Aristotle had already recorded.[146] According to Schmitt, the contrast between these two

---

144  Cremonini 1627, 52: "Tunc scilicet est perfecta, quando ad eum terminum venit, in quo sufficienter et egregie deserviat proprio usui. Quocirca, dicere illam esse perfectam, quando fuerint inventi parvi quidam musculi non animadversi ab aliis; aliquae glandulae, quas alii non videruntet quaedam parvae cavitates pro faciendis spiritibus, non est dicere de illius perfectione, quia istae minutiae nihil sunt et non deserviuntalicui cognitioni, aut operationi illarum Artium et Scientiarum, quarum gratia haec exercentur in dissectione; et vos id per vos ipsos facile videbitis. Quaerunt enim usus remotissimos et vix, ac multa vi aliquos inveniunt. Igitur ista Ars, cui tantum insistit Galenus, potest etiam ipsa habere aliquos defectus, ex quibus nisi intellectu et ratione succurramus, facile possumus incidere in errores."

A parallel case can be made of magnetism as Stephen Pumfrey has shown in his illuminating article on the subject. Neo-Aristotelian, Niccolo Cabeo, wrote a book *Philosophia magnetica* in 1629, where he criticized the views of William Gilbert as stated in *De magnete* (1600). Cabeo attacks Gilbert on the ground that the demonstrations he uses are only demonstrations of the existence of an fact (*demonstratio quia*), not demonstrations of why it exists (*demonstratio propter quid*). Cabeo maintains that only Aristotelian natural philosophy can produce reasons for natural phenomena. Pumfrey 1990, 181–182.

145  This position is clearly spelled out in Zabarella's introductory lecture for the academic year 1585, Schmitt 1983a, 11: "I will never be satisfied with Aristotle's authority alone to establish something, but I will always rely upon reason; such a thing is truly both natural and philosophical for us, and I will al so seem to imitate Aristotle in using reason, for in fact he seems never to have put forward a position without utilizing reason." Translation by Charle B. Schmitt. Quotation from MS Milano, Biblioteca Ambrosiana D. 481. inf, published in *"Una oratio programmatica di G. Zabarella"* 1966 (a cura di Mario dal Pra), 290.

146  Once, in reply to charges of heterodoxy by the Inquisistion, Cremonini stated how he saw his role as a teacher: "I cannot, nor do I wish to retract my expositions of Aristotle, since I understand them to be as I interpret them and I am being paid to expound Aristotle insofar as I understand him." Cited from Schmitt 1983a, 11.

174

approaches to Aristotelian philosophy can be elaborated even further. In his view Zabarella frequently relied upon observational (if not experimental) knowledge, but Cremonini practically never, Zabarella was willing to look outside the Aristotelian tradition for materials in his search for the truth, but Cremonini generally not. Schmitt considers Zabarella's approach critical and Cremonini's slavishly literal. The latter led, in Schmitt's view, to the scholastic sterility of later centuries.[147]

John Herman Randall maintained in the 1940's and again in the 1960's that the methodology developed at the University of Padua during the sixteenth century was basically the same as that which Galileo Galilei used in his physics, and that thus it had a large impact on modern science.[148] William Edwards has recently maintained that we should turn our attention from Galileo to Hobbes and Descartes, since, according to Edwards, they also used the basic Aristotelian concepts of science in their methodology.[149]

In a recent article, however, J. Prins has convincingly shown that even if Zabarella and Hobbes partly used the same terminology, their basic approaches to science are totally incompatible. Zabarella's and Hobbes' views differed with regard to the nature and function of logic. Hobbes did not recognize Zabarella's strict division between arts and sciences: for him logic was both an operational art and a cogitative science.[150] Unlike Zabarella, Hobbes' philosophy tried to integrate the oppositions

---

147 Schmitt 1983a, 12. I think Schmitt somewhat exaggerates the difference between these two philosophers. In his view Zabarella emphasized observation of the external world as a source of knowledge, but my interpretation of Zabarella's philosophy does not support this claim. Philip L. Drew has also made an interpretation of Zabarella's and Cremonini's philosophy of nature, where he wants to see them as some kind of pedagogical learning process. Unfortunately, his interpretation does not make much sense to me. See Drew 1983.

148 Randall 1961.

149 For Edwards, however, the scientific methodology of these philosophers remains a topic separated from the larger philosophical framework of their work. Edwards 1983, see also Van de Pitte 1981.

150 Prins 1990, 31: "So, whereas Zabarella considers logic an instrument for the arrangement of notions that, thanks to its metaphysical foundation, enables the scientist to reveal objective reality, to Hobbes logic is a technical science or scientific technology of language by means of which the scientist can construct and consolidate truth itself." See also Walton 1987 and Hanson 1990.

between the order of nature and the order of knowledge, pure and applied science, and between the acquisition and transmission of knowledge.[151] In the Aristotelian concept of science we could have firm knowledge only of the theoretical sciences: natural philosophy, mathematics and metaphysics; but in this new emerging model since nature is not conceived of as an artifact, it is unknown and unknowable. This meant of course a change in what we are really able to know. According to Hobbes, for example, only those things which are made by human beings can be known for sure, which picture is far from Zabarella's notion of science, even if both writers require necessity in a science.[152]

Thus it is no use speaking of verbal similarities between Hobbes' and Zabarella's methodological concepts, as Edwards does, if the use and function of their philosophical systems are totally different.[153] The so-called Randall-dispute thus loses much of its relevance if there is no semantic continuity between the words like *"methodus"* and *"scientia"* as used by sixteenth-century Aristotelians and seventeenth-century representatives of the new scientific movement.[154] In Zabarella's scientific model theoretical fore-knowledge and its practical implications are not different aspects of the same scientific process, for practice is always of minor importance and subject to theory. As Nicholas Jardine has pointed out, only when the solution of practical problems go hand in hand with the formulation of general principles, can we speak of science in the modern sense of the term.[155]

The distinction between theoretical sciences and practical or productive disciplines has ethical consequences as well. In the Zabarellian model the scientist organizes an already existing world, but as a mere spectator does not take part in forming or

---

151  Ibid, 42–43.
152  Rossi 1975, 252–253; Rossi 1983, 138–140.
153  See, for example, Edwards 1983, 212: "But the concepts are Zabarellian". Also at page 216: "But the outlines of the Zabarellian doctrine of method are there, as is – to a surprising extent – the terminology, and some of the considerations that typically appear in Aristotelian discussions of method in e.g., natural philosophy (as opposed to method in mathematics)." In fact, Edwards' suggestion is not a very novel one, because already Watkins, 1965, tried to point out the connection between Hobbes and the Paduan Aristotelians.
154  On this point see especially Pérez-Ramos 1988, 225; Rossi 1983; N. Jardine 1976.
155  N. Jardine 1976, 314–315.

changing it.[156] On the other hand the productive arts imply a active role for the producer: he cannot only follow the productive process, but must take part in it, even beforehand, perhaps, establishing its aims. Thus in the Baconian sense the artist becomes an active manipulator of the world according to his own needs.

This power to change the world, however, places another duty on the producer, namely his responsibility towards nature and other human beings. Perhaps only recently has mankind wholly understood this ethical responsibility, but some Renaissance authors were already emphasizing the need for practical reform of the sciences on ethical grounds. Niccolo Leoniceno, for example, wrote that medicine has a practical end, namely saving human lives, and that the knowledge of the classical authors and medical practice was essential in order to fulfil their duty properly.[157] Juan Luis Vives has stated this attitude most powerfully:

> If something is stated erroneously by one theologian it is corrected by another; if a jurist makes a mistake it is put right by the equity of the law, with restitution of the whole ... but if an error is made by a physician, who will correct it? Who will bring a remedy to a dead man?[158]

---

156  Hans Blumenberg has described it as a "Zuschauer-modell" of science. See Schmidt-Biggeman 1983, 68, 80–81. Paolo Rossi has stated that in this Aristotelian system of science there is place for only two people: the master and the pupil, not for the inventor of new things. Rossi 1983, 150.
157  Of these aspects of Leoniceno's medical reform see Bylebyl 1979, 341; 1985, 38–39.
158  Juan Luis Vives, *De tradendis disciplinis* 4.6, 1531, *Opera VI*, 380. Cited in Siraisi 1988, 229; translation by Nancy G. Siraisi.

# 7. Arts and sciences at Padua in the sixteenth century

In all the points that Zabarella took up in his *Opera logica* there is a common factor; the nature of scientific knowledge (*scientia*) is always considered. Whether he wrote about logic or poetry, medicine or mechanics, he always considered their relationship to the theoretical sciences, especially to philosophy of nature which was at the centre of his interest. Another important connection is that in these discussions he never tired of making the distinction between the theoretical sciences and the practical or the productive disciplines, namely the arts. Indeed, this distinction penetrates the whole of his philosophy.

Zabarella's emphasis on the theoretical branches of knowledge separates his concept of science from that of the humanists. In contrast to their *Quattrocento* colleagues, the sixteenth-century humanists were more interested in the actual content of classical writings, not merely in their grammatical or other textual form. The humanistically orientated writers paid gradually more attention to the practical usefulness of arts than to the theoretical sciences. Consequently this led to the birth of some new disciplines and to a revitalization of some older ones.

At the beginning of his *Opera logica* Zabarella makes clear that logic is above all an instrument of the theoretical sciences and can only accidentally be used to help the practical and productive disciplines. On the same ground the art of demonstration is the main instrument of the theoretical sciences; dialectics and topics come afterwards. Rhetoric and poetry are the slightest parts of logic, because they are only instruments of politics instead of the more noble theoretical sciences.

Zabarella does not want to mention the concepts of good and bad in defining the end of rhetoric and poetry. This stems from the idea that these are logical disciplines which deal with propositions, not directly with human action, and propositions ought to be considered to be truth or false, not good or bad. On the other hand, Zabarella agreed with the humanistically orientated commentators on Aristotle's *Rhetoric* and *Poetics* that the relevance of these disciplines depended totally on their usefulness to the moral disciplines, above all politics. Zabarella did not emphasize mere delight as a proper end for poetry. Unlike humanists, however, Zabarella did not consider the art of history worth writing at all.

In his methodology, too, Zabarella points out repeatedly that arts and sciences have different methods: resolutive method is proper for the arts and compositive for the sciences. The same is true of orders of presentation: arts are systematized in resolutive order and sciences in compositive order. As a matter of fact, these methods are meant to produce complete knowledge, and thus are used in the arts only on the grounds of analogy. Zabarella states that all knowledge depends on sense-perception, but far more important for his consideration of regress-method is the abstraction of the universal made by agent and passive intellects together.

The distinction between theoretical and practical spheres not only concerns Zabarella's methodology, but is even more fundamental in his works on natural sciences and his classification of different disciplines. Science (*scientia*) is a close system built on necessary knowledge, where the work of a scientist is to arrange knowledge in this formally perfect system of the natural world. An art (*ars*), however, has nothing to do within this system. The end of the arts is not knowledge but operation, which is based on the information the sciences have produced because, for the major part at least, the sciences produce the principles for the lower arts. At the same time this distinction is hierarchical: the knowledge used in the arts is only contingent, not necessary, and their methods are not capable of producing perfect scientific knowledge.

If the arts and sciences are so clearly separated, it inevitably has consequences for the theory of scientific progress. At the beginning of the sixteenth century the break between arts and sciences was not so fundamental, according to such writings as those of Nico-letto Vernia, Alessandro Achillini and Agostino Nifo. Vernia and Achillini considered medicine both a theoretical and practical discipline, and they even classified it as a science in the proper meaning of the word. Even if the difference between arts and sciences was emphasized, as in Manardi's commentary of Galen's *Ars medica*, he explicitly pointed out that arts are by no means of inferior value compared with the theoretical sciences. On the other hand, in Zabarella's philosophy the arts are restricted only to the manual production of artefacts, with no connections to scientific progress; whereas the function of the sciences is only to arrange knowledge in a ready-made Aristotelian universe with no real connection to scientific innovations and discoveries in the modern sense of these words.

Zabarella himself applied his division between theory and practice also to the relationship between natural philosophy and medicine, a theory which separated him from the so-called medical humanists. In these medical writings the theoretical and practical sides of medicine were not usually separated very strictly, so that medicine was often considered as a science, not just a productive art. Another main feature of this medical humanism was that, instead of theoretical physiology, new anatomical observations were considered take the basis of the latter parts of medicine. For Zabarella, however, the medical knowledge arrived at by natural philosophy could be the only basis for the education of medical practioners, not anatomical observations. On this ground the first theoretical part of medicine, physiology, should be considered natural philosophy, not medicine, where the aim is wholly operational. The famous saying "a physician begins where a philosopher stops" (*ubi desinit philosophus, ibi incipit medicus*) identified for Zabarella a hierarchical line of demarcation between two different types of knowledge.

Zabarella was not so eager to separate mechanics from the theoretical sciences, because he considered it to be a sub-alternative part of mathematics, and Zabarella's concept of the philosophy of nature did not include mathematical speculations. Besides Zabarella would have found it difficult to show how this productive discipline, which was at least partly concerned with non-natural motions and was practised for human practical purposes, not for the sake of knowledge, could be counted among the sciences.

On the other hand, even the concept of science held by Zabarella's adversaries was not very "modern". Like Zabarella, most of them considered the theoretical *scientia* as the model for scientific knowledge, but, at least some of them, considered practical and productive disciplines of equal importance to the speculative sciences. None of these Paduan writers really called the Aristotelian scientific framework into question, however. They simply wanted to supplement it with some fresh materials. These humanistically orientated writers tried to legitimize these new practical branches of knowledge, like anatomy and mechanics; to find for them a proper place in the prevailing hierarchy of all arts and sciences. In other words, they wanted to add these parts of knowledge, which they themselves found useful and important, to the ready-made and well-organized system of Aristotelian natural science, of which Fabricius' "Aristotle project" is a good example.

Keeping in mind the distinction between arts and sciences, the aftermath of Zabarella's philosophy has also to be seen in a different light. It leads to results that are quite contrary to the so-called Randall-thesis about the meaning of Paduan Aristotelians to the birth of modern science. Zabarella's orthodox Aristotelianism cannot thus be seen as a forerunner of the seventeenth century concept of science, at least not in any deep sense; even though there may be some verbal similarities. With a hostile general attitude, such as that of Cremonini, to other kinds of knowledge besides that classified as scientific, there is not much place for a revaluation of the scientific system or the hierarchy of disciplines in Paduan Aristotelianism. Zabarella's philosophy was used above all in the text-books on natural philosophy at the turn of the seventeenth century, and his logic and methodology were adopted in protestant Germany to legitimate the new protestant theology. Moreover, in the twentieth century Zabarella's commentary on the *Posterior Analytics* is still considered as one of the best commentaries on Aristotle's text.

# Abbreviations

| | |
|---|---|
| AB | Archiv für Begriffsgeschichte |
| AGP | Archiv für Geschichte der Philosophie |
| AOAC | Aristotelis Opera cum Averrois commentariis. Venice 1562–74. (Facsimile-edition Frankfurt am Main 1962). |
| AV | Aristotelismo veneto e scienza moderna I–II. A cura di L.Olivieri. Padua 1983. |
| BJHS | The British Journal for the History of Science |
| CHLMP | The Cambridge History of Later Medieval Philosophy |
| CHRP | The Cambridge History of Renaissance Philosophy |
| DSB | Dictionary of Scientific Biography 16 volumes. New York 1970–1980. |
| GCFI | Giornale critico della filosofia italiana |
| JHI | Journal of the History of Ideas |
| JHP | Journal of the History of Philosophy |
| QSUP | Quaderni per la storia dell'universita di Padova |
| RCSF | Rivista critica di storia della filosofia |
| RQ | Renaissance Quarterly |
| SHPS | Studies in History and Philosophy of Science |
| SR | Studies in the Renaissance |
| WF | Wolfenbütteler Forschungen |

# Bibliography

## Printed sources

Achillini, A. (1545) *Opera omnia*, Venice.

Alexander of Aphrodisias (1573) *In octo Topicorum Aristotelis libros explanatio*, Venice.

Ammonius Hermeias (1569) *In Porphyrii Institutionem Aristotelis Categorias et librum De interpretatione*, Venice.

Averrois (1550) *In libros Rhetoricum Aristotelis paraphrases*. AOAC, vol. II, Venice.

– – (1550) *Paraphrasis in librum Poeticae Aristotelis*. AOAC, vol. II, Venice.

– – (1550) *De physico auditu libri octo*. AOAC, vol. IV, Venice.

– – (1552) *Epitome in librum Metaphysicae Aristotelis*. AOAC, vol. VIII, Venice.

Balduino, G. (1563) *Expositio in libellum Porphyrii de quinque vocibus*, Venice.

– – (1569) *Variis generis in logica quaesita*, Venice.

Benedetti, A. (1528) *Anatomice, sive de hystoriia corporis humani*, Argentorati (Strasbourg).

Capodivacca, G. (1603) *Opera omnia*, Frankfurt.

da Carpi, B. (1521) *Commentaria cum amplissimis additionibus super anatomia Mundini*, Bologna.

Crellius, F. (1584) *Isagoge logica*, Neustadt.

Cremonini, C. (1627) *Apologia dictorum Aristotelis de origine et principatu membrorum adversus Galenum*, Venice.

– – (1663) *Logica sive Dialectica*, Venice.

De Guevara, I. (1627) *In Aristotelis Mechanicas commentarii*, Rome.

Degli Oddi, Oddo (1574) *In librum Artis medicinalis Galeni*, Venice.

Descartes, R. (1985) *The Philosophical Writings I*. Cambridge.

Duns Scotus (1968) *Opera omnia*, Hildesheim.

Falloppio, G. (1584) *Opera omnia*, Frankfurt.

Galenos, C. (1821) *Opera omnia I*. C. G. Kühn (ed.), Leipzig.

– – (1959) *On anatomical procedures* (ed. by C. Singer), London.

Galilei, G. (1588) *Tractatione de praecognitionibus et praecognitis, Tractatione de demonstratione*. Transcribed by W. Edwards, notes and commentary by W. Wallace, Padua 1988.

*Hippocratic Writings* (1977), Harmondsworth.

Jungius, J. (1957) *Logica hamburgensis,* Hamburg (1638).

Landi, B. (1605) *Anatomiae corporis humani,* Frankfurt.

Leoniceno, N. (1509) *De tribus doctrinis ordinatis,* Ferrara.

Leonico Tomeo, N. (1525) *Opuscula,* Venice.

Maggi, V. and Lombardi, B. (1550) *In Aristotelis librum De Poetica communes explanationes,* Venice.

Manardi, G. (1536) *In primum Artis parvae Galeni librum commentaria,* Basel.

Martini, C. (1623) *Commentariorum logicorum adversus Ramistas libri V,* Helmstedt.

Montanus, I. B. (1556) *In artem parvam Galeni explicationes,* Lyon.

Nifo, A. (1535) *Prima pars opusculorum,* Venice.

– – (1569) *Super octolibros De physico audito,* Venice.

Ockham, W. (1974) *Opera philosophica,* St.Bonaventure.

Pace, J. (1596) *Institutiones logicae,* Speyer.

Paterno, B. (1596) *Explanationes in primam fen primi Canonis Avicennae,* Venice.

Petrella, B. (1584) *Logicarum disputationum libri septem,* Padua.

Philoponus, J. (1553) *In libros Priorum resolutivorum Aristotelis commentarie annotationes,* Venice.

Piccolomini, A. (1551) *L'instrumento de la filosofia,* Rome.

– – (1565) *In Mechanicas quaestiones Aristotelis paraphrasis,* Venice.

– – (1575) *Annotationi nel libro della Poetica d'Aristotile,* Vinegia.

– – (1585) *Della filosofia naturale,* Venice.

Piccolomini, F. (1595) *Universa philosophia de moribus,* Frankfurt.

– – (1603) *Discursus ad universam logicam attinens,* Marburg.

Pietro d'Abano (1565) *Conciliator differentiarum philosophorum et praecipue medicorum,* Venice.

Riccoboni, A. (1587) *Paraphrasis in Poeticam Aristotelis,* Padua.

– – (1595) *De usu Artis Rhetoricae Aristotelis commentarii,* Frankfurt.

Robortello, F. (1548) *In librum Aristotelis de arte Poetica explicationes,* Florence.

Santorio, S. (1602) *Commentaria in Artem medicinalem Galeni,* Venice.

– – (1660) *Opera omnia III,* Venice.

Simplicius (1566) *Commentaria in octo libros Aristotelis De physico auditu,* Venice. Themistius (1549) *Paraphrasis in Aristotelis Physices,* Venice.

Thomas Aquinas (1955) *Expositio super librum Boethii De Trinitate.* Leiden.

– – (1955) *In Aristotelis libros Peri Hermenias et Posteriorum Analyticorum Expositio.* Turin.

Thyus (Tio), A. (1547) *Quaesitum et praecognitiones libri Praedicamentorum Porphirii,* Padua.

Tomitano B. (1562), *Contradictionum solutiones in Aristotelis et Averrois dicta.* AOAC, vol. I, part 3, Venice.

Vernia, N. (1486) *Quaestio est, an medicina nobilior atque praestantior sit iure civili.* La disputa delle arti nel Quattrocento (a cura di E. Garin), Florence, pp. 111–123.

Zabarella, J. (1590) *De rebus naturalibus libri XXX,* Cologne.

– – (1597) *Opera logica,* Hildesheim.

– – (1601) *In libros Aristotelis Physicorum commentarii,* Venice.

-- (1605) *In tres libros De Anima commentarii*, Venice.

-- (1966) *Una "oratio" programmatica di G. Zabarella* (a cura di M. Dal Pra), RCSF 21, pp. 286–291.

Zerbi, G. (1502) *Liber anathomie corporis humani et singulorum membrorum illius*. Venice.

Zimara M. A. (1556) *Theorematum seu memorabilium propositionum Aristotelis et Averrois*, Venice.

-- (1565) *Tabula et dilucidationes in dicta Aristotelis et Averrois*, Venice.

# Literature

Aguzzi-Barbagli, D. (1988) *Humanism and Poetics*. Renaissance Humanism, vol.3 (ed. by A. Rabil Jr. ), Philadelphia, pp. 85–169.

Alessio, F. (1965) *La filosofia e le "artes mechanicae" nel secolo XII*, Studi medievali 10, pp. 69–161.

Antonaci, A. (1971) *Ricerche sull'aristotelismo del rinascimento. Marcantonio Zimara. Volume I: dal primo periodo padovano al periodo presalernitano*. Lecce.

-- (1978) *Ricerche sull'aristotelismo del rinascimento. Marcantonio Zimara. Volume II: dal periodo salernitano al secondo periodo padovano*. Lecce.

-- (1983) *Aristotelismo e scienza medica a Padova nel primo Cinquecento. Il pensiero medico di Marcantonio Zimara*. AV I, pp. 415–434.

*Aristotle Transformed. The Ancient Commentators and their Influence* (1990), (ed. by R. Sorabji), London.

Ashworth, E. J. (1974) *Language and Logic in the Post-Medieval Period*, Dordrecht and Boston.

-- (1982) *The Eclipse of Medieval Logic*. CHLMP, pp. 787–796.

-- (1988a) *Changes in Logic Textbooks from 1500–1650: The New Aristotelianism*. Aristotelismus und Renaissance, WF 40, Wiesbaden, pp. 75–87.

-- (1988b) *Traditional Logic*. CHRP, pp. 143–172.

Baldini A. E. (1980a) *Per la biografia di Francesco Piccolomini*, Rinascimento, serie 2, 20, pp. 389–420.

Balme, D. M. (1972) *Aristotle's De partibus animalium I and De Generatione animalium I*, (translated with notes by D. M. Balme), Oxford.

Barnes, J. (1975) *Aristotle's Theory of Demonstration*. Articles on Aristotle, vol. 1:Science, (J. Barnes, M. Schofield and R. Sorabji eds.), London, pp. 65–87.

-- (1981) *Proof and the Syllogism*. Aristotle on Science: The Posterior Analytics (ed. by E. Berti), Padua, pp. 17–59.

Bartels, K. (1965) *Der Begriff Techne bei Aristoteles.* Synusia (hrsg. von H. Flashar und K. Gaiser), Pfullingen, pp. 275–287.

Beardsley M. C. (1966) *Aesthetics from Classical Greece to the Present. A Short History*, Tuscaloosa and London.

Bialostocki, J. (1963) *The Renaissance Concept of Nature and Antiquity*. The Renaissance and Mannerism. Studies in Western Art II, Princeton, pp. 19–30.

Black, D. L. (1990) *Logic and Aristotle's Rhetoric and Poetics in Medieval Arabic Philosophy*. Leiden.

Blumenberg, H. (1957) *Nachahmung der Natur*. Studium Generale 10, pp. 266–283.

Boas, M. (1962) *The Scientific Renaissance 1450–1630*. London.
Bottin, F. (1972) *La teoria del "regressus" in Giacomo Zabarella*. Saggi e ricerche su Aristotele, S. Bernardo, Zabarella ... (a cura di C. Giacon), Padua, pp. 49–70.
– – (1973) *Nota sulla natura della logica in Giacomo Zabarella*, GCFI 52, pp. 39–51.
– – (1979) *L'opera logica di Giacomo Zabarella e gli scotisti padovani del XVII secolo*. La tradizione scotista Veneto-Padovana (a cura di C. Bérubé), Padua, pp. 283–288.
Boylan, M. (1984) *The Place of Nature in Aristotle's Teleology*, Apeiron 18, pp. 126–140.
Brink C. O. (1971) *Horace on Poetry. The Ars poetica*, Cambridge.
Bruni, F. (1967) *Sperone Speroni e l'Accademia degli Infiammati*, Filologia e letteratura 13, pp. 24–71.
Bruyère, N. (1984) *Méthode et dialectique dans l'oeuvre de La Ramée*, Paris.
Burke, P. (1990) *The Spread of Italian Humanism*. The Impact of Humanism on Western Europe (eds. A. Goodman and A. MacKay), London and New York, pp. 1–22.
Burnyeat M. (1981) *Aristotle on Understanding Knowledge*. Aristotle on Science: The Posterior Analytics (ed. E. Berti), Padua, pp. 97–139.
Butcher S. H. (1898) *Aristotle's Theory of Poetry and Fine Art*, London.
Butterworth C. E. (1986) *Averroes' Middle Commentary on Aristotle's Poetics* (translation, introduction and notes by C. E. Butterworth), Princeton.
Bylebyl, J. (1979) *The school of Padua: Humanistic Medicine in the Sixteenth Century*. Webster, C. (ed.) Health, Medicine and Mortality in the Sixteenth Century, Cambridge, pp. 335–370.
– – (1985) *Medicine, Philosophy and Humanism in Renaissance Italy*. Science and the Arts in the Renaissance (ed. by J. W. Shirley and F. D. Hoeniger), Washington D. C. and London, pp. 27–49.
– – (1985b) *Disputation and description in the Renaissance Pulse Controversy*. The Medical Renaissance of the Sixteenth Century (eds. A. Wear, R. K. French and I. M. Lonie), Cambridge, pp. 223–245.
Carugo, A. (1983) *Giuseppe Moleto: Mathematics and the Aristotelian Theory of Science at Padua in the Second Half of the 16th-Century*. AV, Padua, pp. 509–517.
Cave T. (1990) *Recognitions. A Study in Poetics*, Oxford.
Cerreta, F. V. (1957a) *Alessandro Piccolomini's Commentary on the Poetics of Aristotle*, SR 4, pp. 139–168.
– – (1957b) *An Account of the Early Life of the Accademia degli Infiammati in the Letters of Alessandro Piccolomini to Benedetto Varchi*, The Romanic Review 48, pp. 249–264.
– – (1960) *Alessandro Piccolomini, letterato e filosofo senese del Cinquecento*, Siena.
Charlton, W. (1970) *Aristotle's Physics, books I and II*, (Translated with introduction and notes by W. Charlton, Oxford.
Clagett, M. (1959) *The Science of Mechanics in the Middle Ages*. Madison.
– – (1964) *Archimedes in the Middle Ages I*. Madison.
Close, A. J. (1969) *Commonplace Theories of Art and Nature in Classical Antiquity and in the Renaissance*, JHI 30, pp. 467–486.

– – (1971) *Philosophical Theories of Art and Nature in Classical Antiquity*, JHI 32, pp. 163–184.

Cochrane, E. (1976) *Science and Humanism in the Italian Renaissance*, American Historical Review 81, pp. 1039–1057.

– – (1981) *Historians and the Historiography in the Italian Renaissance*, Chicago.

Cooper, J. M. (forthcoming) *Ethical-Political Theory in Aristotle's Rhetoric*. An unpublished manuscript.

Cranz F. E. (1976) *Editions of the Latin Aristotle Accompanied by the Commentaries of Averroes*. Philosophy and Humanism: Renaissance Essays in Honor of Paul Oskar Kristeller, Leiden, pp. 116–128.

Crescini, A. (1965) *Le origini del metodo analitico. Il Cinquecento*, Udine.

Cunningham, A. (1985) *Fabricius and the "Aristotle project" in Anatomical Teaching and Research at Padua*. The Medical Renaissance of the Sixteenth Century (eds. A. Wear, R. K. French and I. M. Lonie), Cambridge, pp. 195–222.

Dahiyat I. M. (1974) *Avicenna's Commentary on the Poetics of Aristotle*, Leiden.

Debus A. G. (1982) *Man and Nature in the Renaissance*. Cambridge.

Diffley, P. B. (1988) *Paolo Beni. A Biographical and Critical Study*, Oxford.

Doglio, M. L. (1977) *Retorica e politica nel secondo cinquecento*. Retorica e politica, (a cura di D. Goldin), Padua, pp. 55–77.

Drew, P. L. Jr *Some Notes on Zabarella's and Cremonini's Interpretation of Aristotle's Philosophy of Nature*. In AV, pp. 647–659.

Ebert, T. (1976) *Praxis und poiesis. Zu einer handlungstheoretischen Unterscheidung des Aristoteles*, Zeitschrift für Philosophische Forschung 30, pp. 12–30.

Engberg-Pedersen, T. (1979) *More on Aristotelian Epagoge*. Phronesis 24, pp. 301–319.

(forthcoming) *In What Way Is Aristotelian Rhetoric an Offshoot of Ethics?* An unpublished manuscript.

Eriksson R. (ed.) (1959) *Andreas Vesalius' First Public Anatomy at Bologna 1540. An Eyewitness Report*, Uppsala.

Edwards, W. F. (1960) *The Logic of Iacopo Zabarella (1533–1589).* Unpublished Ph. D. thesis, Columbia University.

(1967) *Randall on the Development of Scientific Method in the School of Padua – a Continuing Reappraisal*. Naturalism and Historical Understanding (ed. by J. P. Anton), pp. 53–68.

– – (1969) *Jacopo Zabarella: A Renaissance Aristotelian's View of Rhetoric and Poetry and their Relation to Philosophy*. Arts libéraux et Philosophie au Moyen Age, Montréal-Paris, pp. 843–854.

– – (1976) *Niccolò Leoniceno and the Origins of Humanist Discussion of Method*. E. P. Mahoney (ed.), Philosophy and Humanism, Leiden, pp. 283–305.

– – (1983) *Paduan Aristotelianism and the Origins of Modern Theories of Method*. AV, pp. 206–220.

Ferrari, G. A. (1977) *L'officina di Aristotele: natura e tecnica nel II libro della "Fisica"*, RCSF 32, pp. 144–173.

Ferrari, G. A. and Vegetti M. (1983) *Science, technology and Medicine in the Classical Tradition*. Information Sources in the History of Science and Medicine (eds. P. Corsi and P. Weindling), London, 197–220.

Fiedler, W. (1978) *Analogiemodelle bei Aristoteles. Untersuchungen zu den Vergleichen zwischen einzelnen Wissenschaften und Kunsten,* Amsterdam.

Frede, M. (1987) *Essays in ancient Philosophy,* Minneapolis.

– – (1990) *An Empiricist View of Knowledge: Memorism.* S. Everson (ed.), Epistemology, Cambridge, pp. 225–250.

French R. K. (1985) *Berengario da Carpi and the Use of Commentary in Anatomical Teaching.* The Medical Renaissance of the Sixteenth Century (eds. A. Wear, R. K. French and I. M. Lonie), Cambridge, pp. 42–74.

Garin, E. (1947) *Introduzione.* La disputa delle arti nel Quattrocento, Florence, pp. xiii–xviii.

– – (1963) *Cultura filosofica toscana e veneta nel Quattrocento.* V. Branca (a cura di), Umanesimo europeo e umanesimo veneziano, Florence, pp. 11–30.

Gilbert, N. W. (1960) *Renaissance Concepts of Method,* New York.

– – (1963) *Galileo and the School of Padua,* JHP 1, pp. 223–231.

Gill, M. L. (1989) *Aristotle on Substance. The Paradox of Unity.* Princeton.

Gotthelf, A. (1987) *First Principles in Aristotle's Parts of Animals.* Philosophical Issues in Aristotle's Biology (ed. by A. Gotthelf and J. G. Lennox), Cambridge, pp. 167–198.

Grafton, A. (1988) *The Availability of Ancient Works,* CHRP, pp. 767–791.

– – (1990) *Humanism, Magic and Science.* The Impact of Humanism on Western Europe (ed. by A. Goodman and A. MacKay), London and New York, pp. 99–117.

Grene, M. (1985) *About the Division of the Sciences* (ed. by A. Gotthelf), Pittsburgh and Bristol, pp. 9–13.

Grmek M. D. (1975) *Santorio Santorio.* DSB XII, 101–104.

Hacking, I. (1975) *The Emergence of Probability,* Cambridge.

Halliwell S. (1986) *Aristotle's Poetics,* London.

Hankinson R. J. (1989) *Galen and the Best of All Possible Worlds.* Classical Quarterly 39, pp. 206–227.

Hanson, D. W. (1990) *The Meaning of "Demonstration" in Hobbes's Science,* History of Political Thought 11, pp. 587–626.

Hardie W. F. R. (1980) *Aristotle's Ethical Theory.* (2. ed.) Oxford.

Hardison O. B. (1970) *The Place of Averroes' Commentary on the Poetics in the History of Medieval Criticism.* Medieval and Renaissance Studies (ed. by J. L. Lievsay), Durham, pp. 57–81.

Hathaway, B. (1952) *The Age of Criticism: The Late Renaissance in Italy,* Ithaca.

Herrick, M. T. (1946) *The Fusion of Horatian and Aristotelian Literary Criticism, 1531–1555,* Urbana.

Hill Cotton, J. (1974) *Giovanni Manardi.* DSB IX, pp. 74–75.

Hintikka, J. (1980) *Aristotelian Induction.* Revue Internationale de Philosophie 34, pp. 422–439.

Hutton J. (1982) *Aristotle's Poetics* (translation, introduction and notes by J. Hutton), New York and London.

Isnardi Parente, M. (1966) *Techne.* Firenze.

Jardine, L. (1974) *Francis Bacon. Discovery and the Art of Discourse,* Cambridge.

– – (1988) *Humanistic Logic,* CHRP, pp. 173–198.

Jardine, N. (1976) *Galileo's Road to Truth and the Demonstrative Regress,* SHPS 7, pp. 277–318.

Kahn, C. H. (1981) *The Role of Nous in the Cognition of First Principles in Posterior Analytics II 19.* Aristotle on Science, the "Posterior Analytics" (ed. by E. Berti), Padua, pp. 385–414.

Kahn, V. (1985) *Rhetoric, Prudence, and Skepticism in the Renaissance.* Ithaca and London.

Kakkuri-Knuuttila M-L. (forthcoming) *Dialectic and Science in Aristotle.* An unpublished manuscript.

Kakkuri-Knuuttila M-L. and Knuuttila S. (1990) *Induction and Conceptual Analysis in Aristotle.* Language, Knowledge and Intentionality. Perspectives on the Philosophy of Jaakko Hintikka. (ed. by L. Haaparanta, M. Kusch and I. Niiniluoto), Helsinki, pp. 294–303.

Kessler, E. (1988) *The Intellective Soul*, CHRP, pp. 485–534.

– – (1990) *The Transformation of Aristotelianism during the Renaissance.* New Perspectives on Renaissance Thought (ed. by J. Henry and S. Hutton), London, pp. 137–147.

Knudsen, C. (1982) *Intentions and Impositions.* CHLMP, pp. 479–495.

Knuuttila, S. (1989a) *Selitykset Aristoteleen Nikomakhoksen etiikkaan*, Helsinki, pp. 207–267.

– – (1989b) *Natural Necessity in John Buridan.* Studies in Medieval Natural Philosophy (ed. by S. Caroti), Florence, pp. 155–176.

(forthcoming) *Remarks on Induction in Aristotle's Dialectic and Rhetoric.* Revue Internationale de Philosophie.

Kosman, L. A. *Animals and Other Beings in Aristotle.* Philosophical Issues in Aristotle's Biology (ed. by A.Gotthelf and J. G. Lennox), Cambridge, pp. 360–391.

Kristeller, P. O. (1951) *The Modern System of the Arts I*, JHI 12, pp. 496–527.

– – (1979) *Renaissance Thought and Its Sources,* New York.

– – (1983) *Rhetoric in Medieval and Renaissance Culture.* Renaissance Eloquence. Studies in the Theory and Practice of Renaissance Rhetoric (ed. by J. J. Murphy), Berkeley and Los Angeles, pp. 1–19.

– – (1988) *Humanism*, CHRP, pp. 113–137.

Kurz, D. (1970) *Akribeia. Das Ideal der Exaktheit bei den Griechen bis Aristoteles*, Göppingen.

Laird, W. R. (1986) *The Scope of Renaissance Mechanics*, Osiris, 2nd series 2, pp. 43–68.

– – (1987) *Giuseppe Moletti's "Dialogue on Mechanics" (1576)*, RQ 40, pp. 209–223.

– – (1991) *Archimedes among the Humanists.* Isis 82, pp. 629–638.

*La disputa delle arti nel Quattrocento.* (1947). A cura di E. Garin. Florence.

*La tradizione scotista Veneto-Padovana.* (1979) A cura di C. Bérubé, Padua.

Lind L. R. (1975) *Studies in Pre-Vesalian Anatomy*, Philadelphia.

Lohr, C. H. (1974) *Renaissance Latin Aristotle Commentaries: Authors A–B.* SR 21, pp. 228–289.

– – (1975) *Authors C.* RQ 28, pp. 689–741.

– – (1976) *Authors D-F.* RQ 29, pp. 714–745.

– – (1977) *Authors G-K.* RQ 30, pp. 681–741.

– – (1978) *Authors L-M.* RQ 31, pp. 532–603.

– – (1979) *Authors N-Ph.* RQ 32, pp. 529–580.

– – (1980) *Authors Pi-Sm.* RQ 33, pp. 623–734.

– – (1982) *Authors So-Z*. RQ 35, pp. 164–256.

– – (1988) *Metaphysics*, CHRP, pp. 537–638.

Long, P. O. (1988) *Humanism and Science*. Renaissance Humanism, vol. 3, (ed. A. Rabil Jr.), Philadelphia.

Lucchetta, F. (1979) *Recenti studi sull'averroismo padovano*. Convegno Internazionale l'Averroismo in Italia, Rome, 91–120.

Mahoney, E. P. (1982) *Metaphysical Foundations of the Hierarchy of Being According to Some Late-Medieval and Renaissance Philosophers*. Philosophies of Existence: Ancient and Medieval (ed.by P.Morewedge), New York, pp. 165–257.

– – (1982b) *Neoplatonism, the Greek Commentators and Renaissance Aristotelianism*. Neoplatonism and Christian Thought (ed. by D. J. O'Meara), Albany, pp. 169–177.

– – (1983a) *Il concetto di gerarchia nella tradizione padovana e nel primo pensiero moderno*. AV, pp. 729–741.

– – (1983b) *Philosophy and Science in Nicoletto Vernia and Agostino Nifo*. A. Poppi (a cura di), Scienza e filosofia all'università di Padova nel Quattrocento, Padua and Trieste, pp. 135–202.

Mansion, A. (1946) *Introduction à la physique aristotélicienne*. Louvain and Paris.

Marangon, P. (1977) *Alle origini dell'aristotelismo padovano (sec.XII–XIII)*, Padova.

McKirahan Jr, R. D. (1978) *Aristotle's Subordinate Sciences*, BJHS 11, pp. 197–220.

*Medieval Literary Theory and Criticism (c.1100–c.1375)* (eds. by A. J. Minnis and A. B. Scott), Oxford.

Mendelsohn, L. (1982) *Paragoni. Benedetto Varchis's Due Lezzioni and Cinquecento Art Theory*, Ann Arbor.

Meyer, H. (1919) *Natur und Kunst bei Aristoteles*, Paderborn.

Miesen, K–J. (1967) *Die Frage nach dem Wahren, dem Guten und dem Schönen in der Dichtung in der Kontroverse zwischen Robortello und Lombardi und Maggi um die "Poetik" des Aristoteles*, Warendorf.

Mittelstrass, J. (1988) *Nature and Science in the Middle Ages*. R. S. Woolhouse (ed.), Metaphysics and Philosophy of Science in the Seventeenth and Eighteenth Centuries, Dordrecht, pp. 17–43.

Mugnai Carrara, D. (1979) *Profilo di Nicolo Leoniceno*. Interpres 2, pp. 169–212.

– – (1983) *Una polemica umanistico-scolastica circa l'interpretazione delle tre dottrine ordinate di Galeno*. Annali dell'Istituto e Museo di Storia della Scienza di Firenze 7, pp. 31–57.

Nardi, B. (1958) *Saggi sull'aristotelismo padovano dal secolo XIV al XVI*. Firenze.

Nauert, C. G. Jr. (1979) *Humanists, Scientists, and Pliny: Changing Approaches to a Classical Author*, American Historical Review 84, pp. 72–85.

Nobis, H.M. (1967) *Frühneuzeitliche Verständnisweisen der Natur und ihr Wandel bis zum 18. Jahrhundert*, AB 11, pp. 37–58.

Nussbaum, M. C. (1986) *The Fragility of Goodness. Luck and ethics in Greek Tragedy and Philosophy*, Cambridge.

Olivieri, L. (1983) *Certezza e gerarchia del sapere. Crisi dell'idea di scientificità nell'aristotelismo del secolo XVI*, Padova.

Ong, W. (1958) *Ramus, Method and the Decay of Dialogue*, Cambridge, Mass.

Ottosson, P-G. (1984) *Scholastic Medicine and Philosophy*, Naples.

Owen, G. E. L. (1985) *Aristotelian Mechanics*. Aristotle on Nature and Living Things (ed. by A. Gotthelf), Pittsburgh and Bristol, pp. 227–245.

Ovitt Jr, G. (1983) *The Status of the Mechanical Arts in Medieval Classifications of Learning*, Viator 14, pp. 89–105.

Pagallo, G. F. (1983) *Di un'inedita "expositio" di Nicoletto Vernia "In posteriorum librum priorem"*. AV, pp. 813–842.

Papuli G. (1967) *Girolamo Balduino. Ricerche sulla logica della Scuola di Padova nel Rinascimento*, Bari.

(1983) *La teoria del "regressus" come metodo scientifico negli autori della Scuola di Padova*, AV I, pp. 221–277.

Park K. and Kessler E. (1988) *The Concept of Psychology*, CHRP, pp. 455–463.

Paschetto, E. (1984) *Pietro d'Abano. Medico e filosofo*, Florence.

Pérez-Ramos, A. (1988) *Francis Bacon's Idea of Science and the Maker's Knowledge Tradition*, Oxford.

Petersen, P. (1921) *Geschichte der Aristotelischen Philosophie im Protestantischen Deutschland*, Leipzig.

Poppi, A. (1969) *Pietro Pomponazzi tra averroismo e galenismo sul problema del "regressus"*, Rivista critica di storia della filosofia 24, pp. 243–267.

– – (1970) *Saggi sul pensiero inedito di Pietro Pomponazzi*. Padua.

– – (1972) *La dottrina della scienza in Giacomo Zabarella*, Padua.

– – (1988) *Il prevalere della "vita activa" nella paideia del Cinquecento*. Rapporti tra le università di Padua e Bologna. Ricerche di filosofia, medicina e scienza, (a cura di L.Rossetti), Trieste.

Premuda, L. (1963) *Un discepolo di Leoniceno tra filologia ed empirismo: G. Manardo e il "libero esame" dei classici della medicina in funzione di più spregiudicati orientamenti metodologici*. Atti del convegno internazionale per la celebrazione della nascita di G. Manardo (1462–1536). Bologna, pp. 43–56.

– – (1983) *Le conquiste metodologiche e tecnico-operative della medicina nella scuola padovana del. sec. XV*. A. Poppi (ed.), Scienza e filosofia all'università di Padova nel Quattrocento, Padua-Trieste, pp. 395–428.

Prins, J. (1990) *Hobbes and the School of Padua: Two Incompatible Approaches of Science*, AGP 72, pp. 26–46.

Pumfrey, S. (1990) *Neo-Aristotelianism and the Magnetic Philosophy*. New Perspectives on Renaissance Thought (eds. J. Henry and S. Hutton), London, pp. 177–189.

Randall, J. H. (1961) *The School of Padua and the Emergence of Modern Science*, Padua.

– – (1976) *Paduan Aristotelianism Reconsidered*. Philosophy and Humanism: Renaissance Essays in Honor of Paul Oskar Kristeller, Leiden, pp. 275–282.

Reeds, K. M. (1976) *Renaissance Humanism and Botany*, Annals of Science 33, pp. 519–542.

Reif, P. (1969) *The Textbook Tradition in Natural Philosophy 1600–1650*, JHI 30, pp. 17–32.

*The Renaissance Philosophy of Man* (1948), E. Cassirer, P. O. Kristeller and J. H. Randall Jr. (eds.), Chicago and London.

Renan, E. (1866) *Averroès et l'averroisme*, Paris.

Risse, W. (1964) *Die Logik der Neuzeit I (1500–1640)*, Stuttgart and Bad Cannstatt.

191

– – (1983) *Zabarellas Methodenlehre*, AV I, pp. 155–172.

Roger, J. (1976) *La situation d'Aristote chez les anatomistes padouans*. Platon et Aristote a la Renaissance, Paris, pp. 217–224.

Rose, P. L. and Drake, S. (1971) *The Pseudo-Aristotelian Questions of Mechanics in Renaissance Culture*, SR 18, pp. 65–104.

Ross W. D. (1964) *Aristotle*. London.

Rossi, P. (1970) *Philosophy, Technology and the Arts in the Early Modern Era*, New York.

– – (1975) *Hermeticism, Rationality and the Scientific Revolution*. M. L. Righini-Bonelli and W. R. Shea (eds.), Reason, Experiment and Mysticism in the Scientific Revolution, London, pp. 247–273.

(1983) *Aristotelici e "moderni": le ipotesi e la natura*, AV, pp. 125–154.

Schmidt, R. W. (1966) *The Domain of Logic According to Saint Thomas Aquinas*. The Hague.

Schmidt-Biggemann, W. (1983) *Topica universalis*, Hamburg.

Schmitt, C. B. (1969) *Experience and Experiment: A Comparison of Zabarella's View with Galileo's in De Motu*, SR 16, pp. 80–138.

– – (1971) *A Critical Survey and Bibliography of Studies on Renaissance Aristotelianism, 1958–1969*, Padua.

– – (1972) *Cicero Scepticus. A Study of the Influence of the Academica in the Renaissance*, The Hague.

– – (1979) *Renaissance Averroism Studied Through the Venetian Editions of Aristotle-Averroes*. L'Averroismo in Italia, Rome, pp. 121–142.

– – (1982) *Andreas Camutius on the Concord of Plato and Aristotle with Scripture*. Neoplatonism and Christian Thought (ed. by D. J. O'Meara), Albany, pp. 178–184.

– – (1983a) *Aristotle and the Renaissance*, Cambridge and London.

– – (1983b) *Aristotelianism in the Veneto and the Origins of Modern Science: Some Considerations on the Problem of Continuity*. AV, pp. 103–123.

– – (1983c) *John Case and Aristotelianism in Renaissance England*, Kingston and Montreal.

– – (1985) *Aristotle among the Physicians*. A. Wear, R. K. French and I. M. Lonie (eds.), The medical renaissance of the sixteenth century, Cambridge, pp. 1–15.

– – (1988) *Towards a History of Renaissance Philosophy*. Aristotelismus und Renaissance (hrsg. von E. Kessler, C. H. Lohr und W. Sparn), WF 40, Wiesbaden, pp. 9–16.

Serene, E. (1982) *Demonstrative Science*. CHLMP, pp. 496–517.

Simionato, G. (1973) *Significato e contenuto delle "Lectiones" del Tomitano nell'evoluzione della logica padovana*. QSUP 6, pp. 111–124.

Siraisi, N. G. (1973) *Arts and Sciences at Padua. The Studium of Padua before 1350*, Toronto.

– – (1981) *Taddeo Alderotti and his Pupils. Two Generations of Italian Medical Learning*, Princeton.

(1987) *Avicenna in Renaissance Italy. The Canon and Medical Teaching in Italian Universities after 1500*, Princeton.

– – (1988) *Medicine, Physiology and Anatomy in Early Sixteenth-Century Critiques of the Arts and Sciences*. New Perspectives on Renaissance Thought (eds. J. Henry and S. Hutton), London, pp. 214–229.

Skulsky, H. (1968) *Paduan Epistemology and the Doctrine of the One Mind*, JHP 6, pp. 341–361.

Smith, W. D. (1979) *The Hippocratic Tradition*, Ithaca and London.

Smithson I. (1983) *The Moral view of Aristotle's Poetics*, JHI 44, 3–17.

Solmsen, F. (1963) *Nature as Craftsman in Greek Thought*, JHI 24, pp. 473–496.

Sorabji, R. (1990) *The Ancient Commentators on Aristotle*. In Aristotle Transformed (ed. by R.Sorabji), London, pp. 1–30.

Sozzi, L. (1981) *Retorica e umanesimo*, Storia d'Italia, annali 4, (a cura di C. Vivanti), Torino, pp. 47–78.

Ste.Croix de G. E. M. (1975) *Aristotle on History and Poetry (Poetics 9, 1451a 36–b11)*. The Ancient Historian and His Materials (ed. by B. Levick), Trowbridge and Esher, pp. 45–58.

Summers, D. (1987) *The Judgement of Sense. Renaissance Naturalism and the Rise of Aesthetics*, Cambridge.

Sylla, E. D. (1979) *The A Posteriori Foundations of Natural Science*. Synthese 40, pp. 147–187.

Tatarkiewicz, W. (1963) *Classification of Arts in Antiquity*, JHI 24, pp. 231–240.

Tayler, E. W. (1964) *Nature and Art in Renaissance Literature*, New York and London.

Taylor, A. E. (1955) *Aristotle*. New York.

Thijssen J. M. M. (1987) *John Buridan and Nicholas of Autrecourt on Causality and Induction*. Traditio 43, pp. 237–255.

Thorndike, L. (1936) *The Debate for Precedence between Medicine and Law: Further Examples from the Fourteenth to the Seventeenth Century*, Romanic Review 27, pp. 185–190.

Tigerstedt, E. N. (1968) *Observations on the Reception of the Aristotelian Poetics in the Latin West*, SR 15, pp. 7–24.

Trinkaus, C. (1990) *Renaissance Ideas and the Idea of the Renaissance*, JHI 51, pp. 667–684.

Wallace, W. A. (1981a) *Aristotle and Galileo: The Uses of Suppositio in Scientific Reasoning*. Studies in Aristotle (ed. D. J. O'Meara), Washington D. C., pp. 47–77.

– – (1981b) *Prelude to Galileo*. Dordrecht and Boston.

– – (1984) *Galileo and His Sources*, Princeton.

– – (1988) *Randall Redivivus: Galileo and the Paduan Aristotelians*, JHI 49, pp.133–149.

Walton, C. (1987) *Hobbes on the Natural and the Artificial*. Hobbes's "Science of Natural Justice" (eds. C. Walton and P. Johnson), Dordrecht, pp. 71–88.

Van de Pitte, F. P. (1981) *Descartes' Revision of the Renaissance Conception of Science*, Vivarium 19, pp. 70–80.

Van Rijen, J. (1989) *Aspects of Aristotle's Logic of Modalities*. Dordrecht.

Vasoli, C. (1968) *Studi sulla cultura del Rinascimento*, Manduria.

– – (1974) *Profezia e ragione*, Naples.

– – (1983) *Giulio Pace e la diffusione europea di alcuni temi aristotelici padovani*, AV, pp. 1009–1034.

– – (1985) *Introduction*. Jacobi Zabarellae De methodis and De regressu (ed. by C. Vasoli), Bologna, pp.xi–xxviii.

Waterlow, S. (1982) *Nature, Change, and Agency in Aristotle's Physics*, Oxford.

Watkins, J. W. N. (1965) *Hobbes's System of Ideas*. New York.

Wear, A. (1973) *Contingency and Logic in Renaissance Anatomy and Physiology*. Unpublished Ph. D. thesis, University of London.

– – (1981) *Galen in the Renaissance*. V. Nutton (ed.), Galen:Problems and Prospects, London, pp. 229–267.

– – (1983) *William Harvey and the "Way of the Anatomists"*. History of Science 21, pp. 223–249.

Weinberg, B. (1961) *A History of Literary Criticism in the Italian Renaissance*, vol. I–II, Chicago.

Weisheipl, J. A. (1965) *Classification of the Sciences in Medieval Thought*, Mediaeval Studies 27, pp. 54–90.

– – (1978) *The Nature, Scope and Classification of the Sciences*. In Science in the Middle Ages (ed. by D. C. Lindberg), Chicago and London, pp. 461–482.

– – (1985) *Nature and Motion in the Middle Ages*, Washington D. C. White Jr, L. (1978) *Medieval Religion and Technology*. Berkeley, Los Angeles and London.

Wians W. (1989) *Aristotle, Demonstration, and Teaching*, Ancient Philosophy 9, pp. 245–253.

Vickers, B. (1988a) *In Defense of Rhetoric*, Oxford.

– – (1988b) *Rhetoric and Poetics*, CHRP, pp. 715–745.

Wieland, W. (1962) *Die aristotelische Physik*. Göttingen.

Witt, R. G. (1983) *Hercules at the Crossroads. The Life, Works and Thought of Coluccio Salutati*, Durham.

Von Fritz, K. (1971) *Grundprobleme der Geschichte der antiken Wissenschaft*. Berlin and New York.

Zambelli, P. (1978) *Aut diabolus aut Achillinus. Fisionomia, astrologia e demonologia nel metodo di un aristotelico*. Rinascimento 18, pp. 59–86.

# Index of names